Vanquishing yellow fever
WALTER REED

Vanquishing yellow fever

WALTER REED

by Edward F. Dolan, Jr.

Illustrated by Dan Siculan

Published by
BRITANNICA BOOKS
a division of
ENCYCLOPAEDIA BRITANNICA, INC., Chicago

TABLE OF CONTENTS

Chapter 1

The Enemy Is Met

The Cuban sunlight on June 25, 1900, was hot and blinding bright, but the doctor paid no attention as he stepped from the small frame shack. He did not even hear the screen door squeak shut behind him, nor did he notice the salute of a passing orderly. His eyes were on the ground, and his heart was heavy with the suffering he had just seen.

The shack was one of the six isolation wards of the hospital at Camp Columbia, the United States Army post situated on a treeless slope near the village of Quemados. Housed in those wards was the killer that the doctor had come hundreds of miles to see, yellow fever.

He breathed deeply of the hot afternoon air. He was a slender man of medium height. His face was narrow, his nose thin and prominent, his cheekbones high, his hair iron grey turning white. His pale blue eyes squinted against the sunlight so that little lines fanned out to his temples. A huge mustache, as gray as his hair, rolled out over his upper lip and swept downward beyond the corners of his mouth; he had a small square chin. This first day on the island he wore a uniform of dress white with a major's gold leaves at the shoulders. He was 49 years old.

He suddenly became conscious of the sounds of the day. Insects buzzed and popped against the screen door. A swarm of cawing birds wheeled in low overhead. A military supply train, moving sluggishly along the tracks to Havana six miles away, rumbled through the gulley separating the isolation wards from the rest of the hospital. But all that was real to him was the slow, whispered groaning of the men in the shack behind him.

Those men—and hundreds more like them—were his reason for being in Cuba. They were United States soldiers who had come south to fight the Spanish-American War, only to fall victim at the war's end to the killer disease that had been on this island since 1649. At present it was raging through Havana and Quemados.

"Wipe it out, Major, before it destroys all of the American occupation force in Cuba, wipe it out—if you can."

Those had been the softly spoken words of Surgeon General George Sternberg, more than a month before in Washington, D.C., words that the brilliant soldier-scientist had then put into the formal language of a written military order.

Major Walter Reed of the United States Army Medical Corps was to proceed by the first available transport to Tampa, Florida, and thence to Camp Columbia, Cuba, where he would take command of a medical commission which was to give special attention to questions relating to the cause and prevention of yellow fever.

Walter Reed lifted his face to a sky of such brilliant blue that it hurt his eyes to look at it. Ever since he had been a boy he had wanted to be of service to mankind, and now he knew that his chance was greater than he had ever dared dream. His orders were to destroy a killer that had stalked the Western Hemisphere for more than two centuries, spreading its evil hand over South, Central, and North America. In the United States alone, it had attacked 500,000 people in the last 100 years and had taken the lives of about 90,000 of them. More than 1,200 U.S. soldiers had felt its touch in Cuba in the past 18 months. More than 200 of them had died. His heart lifted at the idea that he might become responsible for ridding the earth of this evil.

As he stood there in the sunlight, he was confident that yellow fever—or yellow jack as it was more commonly called —could be destroyed. He had good equipment, not the antiquated junk with which earlier investigators had been forced to work. Most important, he had three gifted young doctors under him on the Yellow Fever Commission: Jesse Lazear, James Carroll, and Aristides Agramonte. Without conceit he knew that he himself was nobody's fool in a laboratory; he had been an army doctor for 25 years. He had been professor of bacteriology at the Army Medical School since 1893; and just last year he had headed a research team that had come up with some of the right ideas for the control of typhoid fever in Army camps in the United States. His confidence slumped as the yellow faces in the ward loomed sharp in his mind's eye.

All his previous experience with the fever had been limited to the laboratory. He had never seen an actual case until today. He shuddered. Those yellow faces. That rasping, tortured breathing. Those blooding gums and that terrible nausea. Was it possible that even the best medical skill could put an end to such a powerful, vicious enemy?

The screen door opened, and he turned to see his friend and fellow member of the Yellow Fever Commission, Dr. Jesse Lazear, come down the dirt path to where he stood. Lazear always walked with his shoulders thrust slightly forward, as if he were always getting ready to crash headlong into life. His white smock over his uniform was open and flapped about his knees.

Lazear pressed his hands against the small of his back, stretched, and then shot a glance at Reed from beneath cocked brows.

"Well, what do you think of it, Major?" Lazear had been Major Reed's escort on this first tour of the isolation wards.

Reed shook his head. "It's worse than I had imagined."

"That's the way of it," Lazear said. "You can hear the symptoms described a hundred times over, but you really can't believe them until you've seen them with your own eyes."

"Those yellow faces and eyes. I think they're the hardest things to get used to."

"You'll never get used to them" Lazear said flatly. "You can take the word of anyone down here for that." He nodded toward the shack. "But the boys in there—they're the lucky ones. They're going to recover. No matter how bad they look, their cases aren't fatal."

Even in the harsh sunlight, Lazear's eyes seemed pushed far back into his head, revealing so starkly the purplish stains beneath them. His eyes were glazed over with tiredness. The skin hung loosely about his mouth. All the youth and laughter had gone out of his face. Lazear had looked on too much suffering and too much death in the last six months.

"It's hard to believe that they're not going to die."

"But they're not. In a bad epidemic—and this one is going to be the worst since the Americans arrived in Cuba—approximately 85 out of every 100 cases are doomed. Of that number, the men you've just seen are among the 15 that the fever will let live. They'll be on their feet again in a month. They'll be wasted wrecks, but they'll be alive."

"And immune from another attack for the rest of their lives," Reed added.

Lazear nodded and laughed. It was not a happy laugh, for it did not reach up into his eyes. "That's right. The fever has done them a big favor. If a man survives it, he need never worry about it again. It's quite friendly that way. But come along. I want you to see some really serious cases. Then you'll know for certain the kind of devil our Commission is up against."

Lazear headed toward the shack at the end of the path, and Reed fell in step beside him. Their feet kicked up little puffs of dust. A cooling breeze swept by from the sea a half mile away, cutting some of the heat.

The two doctors made a sharply contrasted pair. Both were the same height, but there the similarity ended. Where Reed was slender, Lazear was thick—in the face and neck, in the shoulders and chest, in the arms and legs. And where Reed was fair and finely cut, Lazear was dark and blunt. He had an olive complexion and a stubby nose. His forehead was broad, with an outthrust ridge running across it just above wide-set brown eyes. His black hair curved down around a full chin, a blacker beard. Both were short-cropped. Lazear was 34 years old. He had a wife and two small children back in the states.

As he walked, head thrust forward in his characteristic way, Lazear went over the symptoms of yellow fever. "It sneaks up on you. At first your patient has a headache and chills, and you think he's coming down with the grippe. Then comes the rising fever, and the nausea and the pains in the back and arms and legs. Those pains give the disease one of its names, *coup de barre*. The blow of a rod. Patients will tell you that they feel as though they're being beaten with a big stick."

Reed smiled patiently. There was no need for Jesse to review the symptoms for him. Reed had heard them often enough and had just now seen them. He knew that Jesse was talking just to be talking. The very thought of yellow jack filled Lazear with a choking rage, and this was a way of getting rid of his fury.

No matter what difficulties lay ahead, Reed knew that he was going to enjoy working with Lazear, one of the most brilliant bacteriologists he had ever met. Lazear had taken his medical degree from the College of Physicians and Surgeons at New York's Columbia University and had later studied in Europe and at Johns Hopkins University. Working in research at Johns Hopkins Hospital at the time war had broken out, he had enlisted in the Medical Corps as a contract doctor, and most of his war service had been spent in Cuba. Because he was an authority on malaria, a disease often confused with yellow jack, he had been chosen to work on the Commission.

Reed had first met him six months ago on a trip to Cuba to check into the effectiveness of a disinfectant that the Army wanted to use. The disinfectant had failed, but Reed never looked on his Cuba trip as a waste; for he had met Lazear, and they had become the closest of friends. They had spent long evening hours in Lazear's cluttered lab at Camp Columbia, sometimes talking of what medicine meant to each of them, sometimes of the great work each dreamed of doing, and often of the latest victories and defeats in the never-ending battle against disease. Lazear's enthusiasm for his work had won Reed's heart. Reed once said, "You can almost see the energy bursting out of Jesse." He thought Lazear a genius, and he was pretty close to being right.

He heard Lazear speaking again. "No one knows how long the first outbreak of the fever will last. Perhaps hours. Perhaps days. The patient is in great pain. The jaundice appears, washing his face yellow. Then, quite suddenly, the fever subsides."

"The period of calm," Reed put in.

Lazear nodded. The breeze from the sea was stronger now. It stirred the flag flying beyond the officers' quarters across the gulley. The breeze felt cool against their faces.

"That's it," Lazear went on. "Your patient gives every appearance of having miraculously recovered, but you know that he's actually come to a very critical point. If he's among the lucky ones, he'll begin to mend. If not, the febrile reaction will set in, the pain and the fever returning. This time they'll be worse—far worse. After that, you know what happens."

His voice trailed away. He stared down at his shoes and the little puffs of dust. Both men indeed knew what happened then.

They had come now to the last ward in the row. Lazear opened the door and stood aside, allowing Reed to enter first. Just inside the door was a wooden table, used as a desk; it was covered with case reports, neatly stacked; off to one side was a metal tray holding upended thermometers. Beside the table, and shoved back against the wall, stood a glass cabinet filled with bandages and medical instruments. Five single beds were placed along either side of a main aisle, all of them reserved for the worst fever cases in the hospital. Halfway down the aisle a wood stove looked like a fat, cast-iron old woman. Considering the weather, Reed thought it the most useless contraption he had ever seen. At the far end of the ward a white screen concealed a bed. The shadows of two people moved behind it.

Reed felt fresh perspiration break out on his forehead. The room was as hot as an oven. The windows along the side walls were flung wide open and the breeze outside was gaining strength, but the coolness had not yet made itself felt in the ward. It was as if the fever were holding it back. The fleshy smell of sickness mingled with the harsh odor of antiseptics. The light in the room was amber.

Lazear stood for a moment at Reed's side. When he spoke it was a hard, flat whisper, the voice of a man who senses that the enemy is too big ever to defeat.

"Four of these men will be dead by Saturday. Two more will go by the middle of next week. As for the rest, perhaps they'll be all right—if they've got the strength to survive and if God is in the mood for a miracle. Nice thought, isn't it, Major? One man will be dead for every one of the next six days. Oh, and there's one more." He motioned towards the white screen at the far end of the ward. "Private Henry Thompson. Alton, Illinois. Nineteen years old. Nice boy. First time away from home. And the last. But maybe he's the most fortunate one of the lot. He'll be out of his misery before sunset today."

The hard whisper was like glass. It cracked. Reed glanced narrowly at Lazear. He could not be sure, but he though he saw tears behind the tiredness in Jesse's eyes. He did not say anything, for he knew Lazear was too proud to like words of comfort. His face looked like a brown stone.

The two doctors walked along the aisle. The men on the beds were covered with white sheets, some motionless, their heads fallen to one side. Others stirred uncomfortably, trying to find some position to make the pain more bearable. The sounds of death closed in on Reed. One groaned. A retching cough came from another. A sharp cry began abruptly and abruptly ended. It was like the cry of a child suddenly hurt. All around Reed was the rasp of dry, harsh breathing.

The faces he saw were far more horrible than those he had seen in the other ward. Their yellow faces seemed yellower, as if the color was pressed deeper into the skin and eyes. There was death in that yellowness. Reed felt all his hope of conquering yellow jack begin to drain out of him. Each bed held a vivid witness of the fever's terrible strength.

[15]

In the first bed, the patient lay flat on his back, his eyes closed. The flesh on his face had wasted away so that it resembled a skull. His burning skin looked so dry that Reed though it would crumble to dust if he touched it, no matter how lightly. The patient lay quite still.

Two beds away, a man trembled uncontrollably, as though he were on an iceberg; but on the pillow beneath his head was the spreading stain of sweat. His head was pushed back deep into the pillow, his chin thrust upwards toward the ceiling. Corded muscles stood out in his neck as he fought for his breath. His arms, outside the sheet that covered him, were stretched taut along his sides. His hands were clenched into fists.

A few steps further, Reed came to a man sobbing like a child. Perhaps it was he who had cried out so piercingly a moment ago. He looked very young, lying on his side, moving spasmodically, first stretching his legs out as if trying to relieve the pain in them or trying to find a cool spot in the bed, and then pulling them back in against his stomach. Through his sobs, he kept repeating a name that Reed could not make out. Blood trickled from the man's mouth and ran down his yellow jaw onto the pillow, making small red-black stains.

The two doctors came at last to the white screen. They stepped around it and found Dr. Roger Post Ames and a nurse standing beside a bed, Ames at the foot, the nurse at the head. The nurse was bent over the patient, and Reed could not see his face.

Ames, who was in charge of the fever wards, smiled a greeting when he saw Reed. They had met briefly on Reed's first visit to Cuba.

[*16*]

Lazear said, "You remember Dr. Reed, sir?"

"Of course. It's good to see you again, Major."

"And it's good to see you, sir."

"When did you arrive?"

"Just this afternoon—by steamer from Tampa."

"Well, we're glad to have you with us. Everyone hopes that you'll be able to do great things down here."

"Thank you, Doctor," Reed said.

Ames saw the look on his face, smiled understandingly, and said softly, "Looks impossible, doesn't it?"

"Yes," Reed admitted.

"Well, you'll be absolutely certain that it is when you've seen Thompson here. He's the worst case on the ward."

Reed moved his eyes to the head of the bed just as the nurse straightened, revealing Thompson's wasted, sweating face. His eyes were closed, and his lips were pulled back in pain. The low, undulating moan of nausea came out of him. The nurse had placed a cold cloth on his forehead, but she had to take it away, for he twisted under it as though it hurt him.

Reed saw that the pillow and the upper part of the sheet that covered him were stained black. A small basin on the nightstand beside the bed was half full of a blackish mess.

Reed swallowed hard, calling up all his professional strength to keep his expression blank. He was looking at the most sickening and most advanced symptom of yellow fever, the black vomit that comes when the disease causes the stomach to hemorrhage.

The nurse was very young, somewhere in her early 20's. She wore a floor-length blue skirt, a striped blouse, and a

white apron. Her apron had lost its starched look; like the
sheet and the pillow, it was stained black. As she tried again
to place the cloth on Thompson's forehead, she made soothing
sounds of the sort a mother makes to a sick child. Her fingers

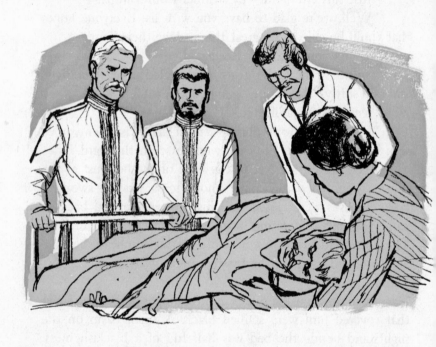

Tenderly the nurse cradled the yellow jack patient to her.

were very gently against his forehead. He struggled away
from them, even tried to lift his hand to push her away.

Suddenly he came up on his elbows, his face contorting,
a new sweat breaking out all over him. He made choking
sounds deep in his throat. His elbows were too weak to sup-

port him, and he started to fall back again. All in one swift movement, the nurse caught his head, cradling it against her bosom, while her free hand took the basin from the nightstand and brought it under his chin. The muscles in his face trembled uncontrollably. The black vomit splashed into the basin and spattered over the nurse's apron. She held him close to her, murmuring soothing sounds.

Reed gripped the steel rail at the foot of the bed. He could not take his eyes off the nurse. A wave of horror swept through him. He believed what every other doctor in the world believed—that yellow fever was caused and spread by microbes. He believed that those microbes were passed from person to person through fomites, the clothes, sheets and pillows that held the emanations and the black vomit of yellow fever victims. The nurse was coolly exposing herself to the death that gripped her patient. Had he tried, Reed could not have found the words to describe her courage.

The spasm passed. Thompson's face smoothed. Still cradling his head against her, the nurse placed the basin on the nightstand and brought a glass of water to his lips. He drank thirstily. When he was done, the nurse lowered his head to the pillow. She wiped away the black from about his mouth, and then she wiped her own hands clean.

Thompson's eyes had been clamped shut all during the ordeal. Now they opened and stared up at the girl. He spoke, softly and with great effort. "I'm sorry."

"Don't talk now," she said gently. "Save your strength."

He smiled, tears standing in his eyes. His voice was almost inaudible. "It'll be over soon, won't it?"

"Very soon," she said. She brushed his hair back, barely

touching his skin with her fingers. "You'll be well again very soon."

"That isn't what I meant. . . ."

His voice faded away, his head fell slowly to one side, his eyes closed. In the midst of the pain and nausea, sleep had come swiftly.

The nurse glanced at Dr. Ames. "He needs new sheets, Doctor. I'll get them now, if I may."

Ames nodded. "But first you'll step outside for a breath of fresh air. You look done in."

The nurse left. The three doctors stood looking down at Thompson for a long moment. Reed felt the intensity of their helplessness. Between them there must have been more than 50 years of practical medical experience. Yet they could do nothing to help the boy on the bed. They were as helpless as if they had never seen the inside of a medical school. To Thompson at this moment, the nurse was far more important than they. At least she could comfort him. Without speaking, they stepped out into the aisle.

The nurse was just disappearing through the front door. She held herself very straight until she was outside. Then, through the screen, Reed saw her shoulders slump and her hand pass absently across her forehead.

"She's no more than a child," Reed said. "How old is she?"

"Twenty-four, I should think," Ames said.

"She shouldn't be here," Reed said. "She's far too young for this sort of thing."

"She's a fine nurse, Doctor. She's been in Cuba a year."

"But did you see her?" Unconsciously Reed pressed his

hands down his sides in a cleansing gesture. "She was exposing herself to the disease, holding that boy in her arms."

"She's taking her chances with the yellow jack, just as are the rest of us," Ames said. He was a tallish, good looking man. He extended a clenched hand to the wooden frame of the screen and tapped it lightly for luck. "So far, our doctors and nurses have been more than fortunate. We've worked in this epidemic for weeks now, and not one of us, with the exception of Major Kean, has fallen ill with the fever. Perhaps God has been looking out for us."

"I hope so."

Ames, eager to get back to his patients, changed the subject. "I imagine that you're checking the wards in preparation for the start of your work with the Commission. Is there anything else I can show you?"

Reed shook his head. "No. No, I think I've seen enough." Enough to last a lifetime, he thought. "Oh, there's just one more thing. Surgeon General Sternberg tells me that you've been very successful in your treatment of the fever. Is there anything special that you've been doing—anything that might be of help to us?"

"I wish I could say that there was. I've just been lucky so far, that's all. The treatment is the same in all cases. Make the patient as comfortable as possible. Use alkaline water and fruit juices. Keep him away from solid foods during the height of the fever. And pray. Pray a great deal, Major."

Reed nodded. "I understand, sir." He smiled suddenly. "Now, you might include the Commission in your prayers."

"I shall, Major. You may count on it."

Reed thanked Ames for his time and, leaving him to

his patient, walked to the front door with Lazear. They stepped out into the sunlight. The breeze from the sea was strong and steady now, and they let it wash over them, luxuriating in its coolness. The nurse stood nearby. She took a deep breath and then went inside the ward, smiling at the two doctors as she passed. There was a moment of silence after she had gone.

Then, with the abruptness so characteristic of him, Lazear said, "Disappointed, aren't you?"

The words so startled Reed that he did not reply immediately, and Jesse pushed on.

"You came down here all full of hopes for killing the fever. Now you've seen it at work and your job looks impossible."

Reed shrugged and smiled. "You know me pretty well, don't you, Jesse."

"Yes, sir. But I also know how I'd feel if I were you." Lazear looked up at the sky. "What about it, Major, can we lick this thing?"

Reed thought the question over. His head was down, and he was seeing again all the things that had passed before his eyes since his arrival at Camp Columbia this June 25th: —the long procession of yellow faces, some sweating with the fever, some dry as dust; bodies twisting and turning with pain; chests heaving with dry, retching coughs; blood coming from broken gums, kidneys, and stomachs; the nurse cradling Thompson against her and exposing herself to what was murdering him; and Ames reciting slowly the useless treatment for the disease.

He saw all these things again, and he knew that hope

was not dead within him. He knew that, as with Lazear, it had become an anger that was now turning into a hard resolve.

When at last Reed did speak he said, "I don't know, Jesse. But this I can tell you: no one is ever going to say that we didn't try."

Chapter 2

The Enemy Reviewed

Immediately upon his arrival at Camp Columbia, Reed had scheduled the first meeting of the Yellow Fever Commission. It was to be held at 3:00 p.m. that same day on the veranda of the officers' quarters on the main grounds of the hospital. Now, with Lazear at his side as he walked away from the isolation wards, Reed took a large gold watch from his breast pocket and squinted at it. The time was 2:45.

"We've got 15 minutes, Jesse, until our meeting," he said.

Lazear sensed what was in his mind. "And you'd like to spend that time by yourself."

"I think so, yes. I've got some thinking to do."

"I imagine that you have," Lazear said, "after what you've just seen."

They stepped onto the footbridge that spanned the gulley separating the isolation wards from the rest of the hospital. The planks underfoot were rough and warped. Below them, railroad tracks glistened dully in the sunlight.

Lazear spoke hesitantly. "Before I leave, I just want you to know one more thing."

"Yes?"

"I'm going to give you all the help you need in this yellow fever thing. Anything you ask of me, I'll do."

Reed smiled and put his hand on Lazear's shoulder. "I know that, Jesse. I knew it from the moment Sternberg told me that you were assigned to the Commission."

"It's going to be like old times, working together in that lab of mine. I'm afraid you'll find it as cluttered as ever," Lazear said. Then, smiling as if embarrassed by his show of affection, he turned and walked swiftly away.

Reed watched him leave the footbridge and move in his thrusting way along the path leading to the distant officers' quarters, a two-story barracks building with a stubble of yellow-green grass circling it. Reed walked to the rail of the footbridge, took off his cap, and felt the afternoon breeze stir coolly in his hair. He set his elbows on the rail and stared down at the tracks.

He had just seen yellow fever at work in the wards. Now, he felt the urge to review the history of the disease. It struck him as necessary to have marshaled in his mind all the available facts about the fever before he told his three doctors how the Commission was going to fight it.

He knew nothing definite about the early history of the disease, nor did he have any idea of how many years it had ravaged the warm climates east beyond the Atlantic; that knowledge was veiled in the confusion rising out of eras that had not yet learned to tell one illness from another. What he did know was that the fever had come to the New World in the 17th century. In the early summer of 1648, the landowners of Barbados Island in the Caribbean Sea took delivery of a cargo of African slaves from a Spanish ship. They had also taken delivery of a consignment of death.

Within a matter of weeks, a mysterious illness struck down and killed hundreds of the bewildered and frightened islanders. The illness then spread northward and westward to the islands of Guadeloupe and St. Christopher. Guadeloupe lay in its grip for 20 months. For want of a better name, the people of the Caribbean called the strange killer Barbados distemper.

The next months saw it leap westward to Yucatan on the Mexican mainland. Hardest hit there was the city of Merida, where the plague raged unchecked for two years straight. A new name accompanied its spread westward. The Spaniards, seeing what it did to their faces, called it yellow fever.

From Yucatan, it swung eastward again, arriving in Havana in the summer of 1649. It attacked the city for weeks and advanced its yellow stain over the entire island of Cuba, dying out at last in the early winter. The people of the Caribbean prayed that it would never return.

But they prayed in vain. The yellow killer liked this New World. It found that the climate suited it perfectly. It continued to reappear year after year, plaguing Cuba and the islands lying off in all directions. It made annual visits to the eastern coast of Mexico and slowly worked its way south along the Isthmus of Panama and forced its way into South America.

Exactly two decades after its arrival in the Western

Hemisphere, yellow fever came to North America. Carried on a ship from the Caribbean, it landed at New York in 1668. Within 100 years it took nearly 3,500 lives there and earned two new names, American plague and malignant infectious fever. From New York it advanced west and south and north. Men, women, and children lay slaughtered in its wake.

Reed remembered reading that the Philadelphia epidemic of 1793 was one of the most tragic of all the early American outbreaks. The fever came in August that year, arriving without warning, as was its custom. Entire families were struck down and wiped out almost overnight. Throughout the city, the yellow paint of pestilence was splashed over front doors. The dead were placed in the streets and, unattended by friends or relatives, were hauled away in carts driven by Negroes. The bodies were dumped in shallow, hastily dug graves at the edge of town. People scattered at the sight of the hearses, and the oldest of friends avoided each other. Some people took to always maneuvering to the windward of anyone they passed in the streets.

Business soon came to a standstill. Stores were boarded up and houses closed as hundreds and then thousands of terrified people fled to the open country, believing, as their forefathers in the Middle Ages had believed, that the only way to avoid the plague was to seek fresh, clean air. Many deserted sick relatives and friends, leaving them to die alone.

But, out in the country, the refugees found no peace, no freedom, from the yellow death. It pursued them and took them wherever it pleased. Some dropped as they staggered along dusty roadways; others managed to crawl into the blessed shade of trees. All of them went without care. Those who stumbled upon them fled in terror. When they died, some of them were buried and some were not. Bodies rotted in the hot, humid sunlight. Food ran short among the refugees. Starvation now joined the fever. The hungry wanderers approached the villages surrounding Philadelphia. The refugees were ready to do the dirtiest of farm work for a crumb of bread. They were ready to beg.

But village mothers screamed and gathered in their children and ran to lock themselves in their cottages. Windows were boarded up and doors bolted against them. Bands of white-faced farmers collected rifles and gestured them away. Others stoned them if they dared come within hailing distance. Medieval fear and brutality was set loose in the newly born United States. Reed could hardly believe that it had happened in his own country. But the record of it—the medical writings and the personal journals of the day—were there for him to see.

The plague went away in the late autumn, only to crop up in other cities in the next years. Within living memory for Reed was the 1878 outbreak in the South. It had hit hardest that year in Memphis, Tennessee, next door to Reed's own native Virginia.

The attack was so vicious that people died faster than they could be buried. It was not unusual for a man, upon waking in the morning, to find two or three of his children dead in bed together. The police force dwindled in number from 47 to 7. As in Philadelphia, shops and houses were boarded up and the citizens took to the open country, choking the roads falling away from the city. And, as in Philadelphia, they were refused help in all the outlying districts.

Then the stricken city fell prey to another kind of plague. Armies of thieves and looters, attracted by the prospect of wealth for the taking, swept down on it, ransacking it from one end to another. They pushed in shop windows and filled their sacks with goods. They drove their wagons up on the lawns of great houses and looted them from attic to cellar. They dumped corpses out of their beds and ripped through the straw mattresses in search of hidden family treasures. They drank the whiskey hauled out of taverns and then staggered through the streets on a rampage of wanton destruction, fighting with each other, and often killing each other.

Eventually the fever took its revenge for the intrusion. It struck them down, leaving many of them to die among the riches they had taken.

The yellow death and the looters were gone by late autumn, and so the citizens of Memphis moved back into their broken city. They looked at their smashed shops and at their ransacked homes. The fever had cost the entire South over $100,000,000 in property destroyed and trade lost that summer.

And what had the doctors been doing during those years when the fever was laying waste the Western Hemisphere? What had they accomplished in the fight against the disease? Nothing. They treated the fever exactly as it had been treated for hundreds of years. Some used charms to drive away the devils of illness. Some fumigated their patients. Some opened the windows wide to let the poison of the disease escape, at the same time closing the windows of the healthy so that the fever could not get in. Some bled their patients to rid them of the 'bad' blood that caused the raging temperatures of the disease. Some merely shrugged and refused to do anything. Yellow fever, they said, was God's revenge on the evil in people; there was nothing to do against an angry God.

The 19th century had produced men such as Louis Pasteur and Robert Koch and Pierre Roux and Joseph Lister, who cried out that disease was not the result of an annoyed God or an imbalance of the chemicals in the body. These men asserted disease was caused by little germs, germs so small that they could not be seen by the naked eye. These tiny germs had the power of giants. They could kill, and they did kill, every day of the year.

But few doctors paid any heed to these early observations, and the germ theory of disease did not take firm hold on the scientific world until after the middle of the 19th century. The Frenchman Pasteur showed the power of the germs —they were soon given the name "microbes"—in such diseases as anthrax, chicken cholera, and hydrophobia. Lister of Edinburgh demonstrated that microbes had the power to kill a patient in an unclean operating room. And Germany's Koch, late in the century, then discovered the germ responsible for tuberculosis.

By the middle of the century, the doctors fighting yellow fever had a definite scientific philosophy on which to base their fight. Their theory was that the germs of the disease were to be found in the blood and intestinal tracts of the stricken. These germs were supposedly passed from person to person through fomites, the bedding and the clothes that carried the emanations and the black vomit and the very breath of the sick, and through the personal possessions of those who came in contact with the sick.

It was a neat, modern theory, and it caught the fancy of the public. They destroyed millions of dollars worth of property on its behalf. Houses that had been visited by the fever were burned to the ground. Bedding and personal possessions of victims were carted away and buried or destroyed. Baggage and clothes from travelers returning from a fever zone were confiscated.

There was only one thing wrong with this neat theory. No one had ever seen the villainous germs. No one, no matter how practiced his eye or how expensive his microscope, had ever found a germ common to all or even several, fever cases. But that did not bother the doctors. They continued to study the blood and the intestinal tissues of the sick, and they continued to insist that it was only a matter of time before the germ was sighted.

Reed knew that several men had come very close to seeing that germ. Surgeon General George Sternberg was one. For 14 years, Sternberg had experimented with all the germs that were suspected of causing yellow fever. He had eliminated as possibilities all but one, which he called bacillus x. But he could not be certain that it was the guilty party, for as yet he was unable to make it produce a case of the disease in a laboratory animal.

There were other investigators. Just three years before, in 1897, the Italian scientist, Giuseppe Sanarelli, after a series of experiments at the Pasteur Institute in Paris, announced that he had discovered the yellow fever villain, a microbe that he called the bacillus icteroide. Among those who doubted Sanarelli's claim was Sternberg. The bacillus icteroide was a germ easily sighted in a microscope and easily grown in laboratory cultures, and Sternberg could not understand how he had overlooked it in 14 years of study.

Sanarelli's bacillus icteroide had first gotten Reed involved with yellow fever. In 1898 Sternberg had set Reed and his assistant, Dr. James Carroll, to the job of proving or disproving the part played by the bacillus icteroide in yellow fever. While at the Army Medical School just one year ago, Reed and Carroll had published a paper proving that Sanarelli's bacillus had nothing to do with yellow fever. They also proved that Sternberg's bacillus x was not the villain.

This was the situation at the very moment that Reed leaned against the rail of the footbridge and stared down at the railroad tracks. Doctors knew of many microbes that had nothing to do with yellow fever, but they had yet to find the germ that was responsible. Surely they would find it. Everyone believed that fomites spread the germs of yellow fever.

Everyone, that is, except a few scientists. They held that yellow fever was carried by insects, mosquitoes. Chief among them was the brilliant old Scotsman, Dr. Carlos Finlay, who had lived in Havana for more years than most people could remember. In 1881, Finlay had informed his startled listeners at the Havana Academy of Sciences that yellow fever was spread by mosquitoes that had been "directly contaminated by stinging a yellow fever patient" or by feeding from his discharge. Few scientists had taken him seriously then, and only a handful continued to take him seriously. In general, this theory was laughed at.

But it was a theory, Reed knew, that could cause his Commission trouble. One of Finlay's most ardent supporters was the vital Jesse Lazear.

[32]

"Major Reed."

Reed lifted his face at the sound of the familiar voice and turned to see Dr. James Carroll walking onto the footbridge. Instinctively, Reed's hand went for his watch.

"Is it time already?"

"Three o'clock straight up, sir," Carroll said. "Agramonte and Lazear are ready and waiting for you."

Carroll's voice was deep and swift. His was a quiet, retiring manner. He was a small man of slender and stringy build but with muscles hard as a rock. His hawklike features were emphatic because he had lost most of his hair. He was 47 years old, the father of five children. A native of England, he had studied medicine while serving as an enlisted man in the Medical Corps and had taken his medical degree from the University of Maryland. He had been Reed's assistant for seven years.

Carroll chuckled far down in his throat. "It looks as if we're going to have quite a crowd of spectators. I think practically every doctor in the hospital has found some excuse to be on the veranda of the officers' quarters."

Reed nodded. "That was to be expected." He set his cap down firmly on his head and took a deep breath. "All right, Jim, let's go."

The two doctors who had just this day arrived from Tampa walked together to the first meeting of a group that hoped to change the medical history of the world.

Chapter 3

A Plan of Battle

As Carroll had predicted, the veranda of the officers' quarters was crowded with doctors. They stood, clad all in white, talking casually to each other and smoking pipes and cigars. They had gathered around four wicker chairs placed in a rough circle near the center of the porch. Several young physicians clustered in the doorway. A short distance from the veranda, a group of orderlies had gathered to watch the proceedings.

When Reed walked up the steps, conversation ceased and the doctors whom Reed had first met six months ago greeted him effusively. He shook hands all around and followed Carroll to the circle of wicker chairs, where Lazear and Dr. Aristides Agramonte were waiting for them. He noticed that Captain A. N. Stark, surgeon in charge of the Quemados district, and Major William Crawford Gorgas, chief sanitary officer at Havana, were there. Reed sat down across from Agramonte, with whom he had eaten lunch. Agramonte was 34 years old, Cuban by birth; he was a darkskinned, soft-spoken man with intelligent, piercing brown eyes. The son of a Cuban army general who had been killed in one of the island's early uprisings against the Spanish, Agramonte had been educated in the United States at the College of Physicians and Surgeons, graduating in the same class with Lazear. His initial professional experience had been in New York City, where he had first worked as an assistant bacteriologist and then as sanitary inspector with the City Health Department. Like Lazear, he had been in Havana since the earliest days of the war. He was currently doing autopsy work on fever cases at Hospital Number One in Havana.

Reed immediately got down to the business of the meeting.

"As you know," he said, "Surgeon General Sternberg has given us the job of looking into the problem of finding the cause and prevention of yellow fever. He feels, as do I, that the first thing we should do is locate the germ responsible for the disease. We have agreed that our first investigations of the fever will be of Sanarelli's bacillus icteroides."

At this statement, Lazear shifted uncomfortably in his chair. He was seated at Reed's left, slumped on the base of his spine. "I thought you and Carroll here had definitely disproved the bacillus icteroides as the cause."

"And so did we," Reed said. "At least, we did to our satisfaction—and to Sternberg's. But . . ." Reed made a wry face. "Apparently we didn't satisfy Sanarelli. He has charged that we were careless in our work."

"That was to be expected," Lazear said. "No man likes

to see his pet theory exploded."

"But there's something else," Reed said. "Just before Sternberg formed the Commission, he received word that two doctors of the United States Marine Hospital claim to have found bacillus icteroides in almost every yellow fever patient they have autopsied."

The words brought a gasp of disbelief from Agramonte. A dark flush crept into his proud face. He ran a finger under his mustache.

"But that can't be! You've read my report, haven't you, Major?"

"Yes."

"Then you know that for many months now, I've been autopsying fever cases over at Hospital Number One. In particular, I have been looking for the bacillus icteroide. I haven't found it once in all the cases I've autopsied. But!" He leaned forward to give his words emphasis. "But I have found the bacillus in many cases that were not yellow fever!"

"I know. Nevertheless, Surgeon General Sternberg feels that, on the basis of the claims made by the Marine Hospital doctors, we cannot completely count out Sanarelli's bacillus. He has given us orders to start with it. If it does not prove itself out swiftly, we are to move on to other things."

The men seated around him, with the exception of Lazear, nodded. Reed pressed his fingers together and studied them for a moment. "And so we will proceed with the first work of the Commission in the following manner. Agramonte, you will continue your autopsy work at Hospital Number One. We'll send to you all patients who die of the fever. Lazear, Carroll, and I will work here at Lazear's laboratory.

Tempers ran high when the Yellow Fever Commission first met.

We'll study blood and tissue samples in the hopes of finding what we're looking for."

He glanced at Carroll, who nodded. And then at Agramonte, who also assented. His eyes came round to Jesse, who was still slouched down carelessly in his chair, regarding Reed quietly. Lazear swept an imaginary bit of dust from his knee. Then he said, quietly and deliberately and respectfully. "Major, I think we'll be wasting our time."

Reed had expected the words, and so he took them calmly. But Carroll came forward in his chair, his hawklike face hard with anger. Jesse's remark was tantamount to an insult, and no one insulted Reed in James Carroll's presence. "I'll ask you to watch your tongue, sir."

Lazear glanced at him from under level brows. He smiled idly. "Calm down, Doctor. No insult was intended. Major Reed knows what I'm getting at."

Reed nodded. "Your mosquito theory."

"Not my theory, Major. Dr. Finlay's theory."

The tension on the porch was replaced by smiles of amusement. One or two of the younger doctors standing in the doorway guffawed. Major Gorgas, looming above Lazear's shoulder, took the cigar from his mouth and yawned. He said, "Not that again, Lazear. Finlay's a wonderful old fellow. A great scientist, really, highly respected. Except in one area. We all think he's a little cracked on this mosquito thing."

Reed looked at Agramonte, who had settled back in his chair. "You're a Cuban by birth, Doctor. Dr. Finlay has been down here all his life. What do your people think of him?"

"It's as Dr. Gorgas explains," Agramonte said. "Finlay is greatly loved by the people. He lives with his wife and an assistant in a great house in Havana. But the people feel that perhaps he isn't quite rational in regard to his mosquito and the yellow fever."

"What's so strange about his mosquito theory?" Lazear demanded. He was still down on his spine with his legs crossed, but his hands were drumming the arms of the chair, and Reed could see Lazear's face. "What's so blessed odd about thinking that a mosquito bite can cause the fever?"

Carroll spoke up. "But it's a well know fact that the fever is spread by fomites."

"Is it?" Lazear demanded, glaring.

"It is."

"No! You say it is fact. But it's not. It's just a belief. And, Doctor, there's a great difference between fact and belief. Don't you agree?"

The two men sat glaring at each other. Reed shifted uncomfortably. The work of the Commission was going to be difficult enough without having these two fine doctors at each other's throats.

Reed asked, "Jesse, why do you hold with the mosquito theory? What facts do you have to back it up?"

"What facts?" Lazear sat up straight now. "Do you really want to hear them?"

"I do."

Lazear hesitated before launching into his explanation. He seemed to be marshaling his thoughts.

"All right, Major. Here they are." Lazear lifted his hand, fingers spread. As he spoke, he knocked over a single finger to emphasize an individual point. "First, the fever never strikes except in the summer; it may last until winter, as it did in the Philadelphia epidemic of 1783, but I challenge you to find one case that has appeared in the winter. It gets under way only when the hot weather is about—when the mosquitoes are out."

"Second, if you've read the journal of Dr. Benjamin Rush."

"I have."

"Then you know that during the Philadelphia epidemic, Rush noticed that there were many mosquitoes about that year. Right, Major?"

"Correct."

Lazear moved on. "Three: Thomas Jefferson wrote that during one epidemic in his area, he saw mosquitoes in abundance. Four: Finlay has found the same thing. Wherever there is yellow fever, you will find mosquitoes. Not just any mosquito, but one in particular. The *Culex fasciatus*."

Lazear's hand dropped to the arm of the chair, making a sharp slapping sound. "And then there's the last point. Medicine has know for a long time that man can contract diseases from mosquitoes. Twenty years ago, Dr. Patrick Manson showed that a certain kind of mosquito spreads filariasis. And just two years back, Dr. Ronald Ross established that the *Anopheles* mosquito is the carrier of malaria. Now, if mosquitoes can spread filariasis and malaria, why can't they carry yellow fever?"

Lazear sat back. He had no more to say. For a moment, there was silence on the veranda. It was broken by Carroll.

"Is that all, Doctor?"

"What do you mean? Is that all? I'll admit that Rush's and Jefferson's comments on the mosquitoes are just interesting observations and perhaps can be discounted on scientific grounds, but you can't ignore the findings of Manson and Ross. And you can't ignore Finlay's theory. He has spent years developing it."

"Very interesting. But I still think that the fomites theory . . ."

"What's so precious about the fomites theory?" Lazear

demanded angrily. "Why is it so impossible to believe that yellow jack can be spread by an insect?"

Reed, pained to see his two good friends clashing headon again, spoke calmly.

"I'll grant you that it's an interesting theory, Jesse. But, like Carroll, I must say that my leanings are toward the fomites theory. It makes a great deal of sense to me. On top of that, General Sternberg has requested that the Commission begin his work by looking again into the matter of the bacillus icteroide. I'm afraid we're going to have to forego the mosquito idea for the time being."

"As you wish, Major," Lazear said softly. His voice was barely audible in his effort to control his anger. "I told you that I would give all the help it was humanly possible for me to give in this work, and I meant it. Now I've got to say one other thing. I think we're being criminally remiss in our duties if we do not look into Finlay's theory. I think we're going to have a lot of dead men on our conscience."

Reed's face stiffened. He deeply believed that fomites spread yellow fever, and he was injured by Jesse's words.

He said as calmly as he could, "I hope not, Jesse. The mosquito theory is interesting, but we are committed to work along certain lines. You believe that mosquitoes spread yellow fever. We are looking for what causes and what spreads it. Surgeon General Sternberg has ordered us to begin with a double check of Sanarelli's bacillus icteroide, in light of the claim by the Marine Hospital doctors that they have found it in fever patients. And so Agramonte will continue his autopsies at Hospital Number One. You and Carroll and I will search for the icteroide in the blood and intestinal tissues. With luck, we will find that the icteroide or some other germ is the killer."

He had spoken softly, but there had been steel in his voice. His words took the form of an order, and as senior officer on the Commission, he expected them to be obeyed.

He glanced from face to face. "Are there any questions, gentlemen?"

No one answered. Lazear and Carroll were glaring at each other. Agramonte was brushing his thin mustache with his fingertips. Reed stood up.

"Then this meeting is at an end. I suggest a good night's rest for us this evening. We'll begin work in the morning."

He was not the kind of man who could leave his friends on a note of ill temper. He said, "I have a feeling that we're going to be successful in our work. Everything is in our favor. With the help of all, we may make yellow fever a thing of the past."

Chapter 4

This Man Reed

I mmediately after dinner, Reed went to his two-room suite on the second floor of the officers' quarters. The rooms were furnished in the Spartan simplicity of all military accomodations. The floors were bare. In a combination study and parlor were a small field desk and several chairs, one of them a rocker. A kerosene lamp stood on the desk. In the other room were a narrow steel cot, a bureau, and a washstand. A mirror hung on the wall directly above the bureau. An orderly had placed Reed's army chest at the foot of the cot and had hung his uniforms in a closet.

When Reed entered the study-parlor, it was lit only by a shaft of moonlight. He did not bother to light the lamp and examine the rooms; he knew exactly what to expect. Twenty-five years of army life had taught him that one set of quarters was no different from another. He took off his tunic, and draped it neatly over the chair at the desk. His legs ached

[43]

dully as he moved the rocker to the window and sat down.

From the veranda directly below came the hum of voices and an occasional burst of laughter. In his immediate view were the twinkling yellow-orange lights of the hospital. Off in the distance was the sea; he caught a whiff of salty sea air whenever the breeze freshened. Overhead the moon was a huge white disk enshrouded in a thin stream of milky clouds.

Reed closed his eyes. The slow back-and-forth motion of the chair, and the soft, rhythmic squeaking of its rockers against the bare floor lulled him to drowsiness. He had come south in the past 48 hours. He had walked through the isolation wards, listening to Jesse Lazear's harsh, flat whisper; he had studied the yellowed faces and watched the young nurse with the effluvia of the fever splashing over her apron.

His head slipped over to one side. He slept the deep sleep of the traveler momentarily at rest. He had come a great distance. He had a greater distance yet to go. . . .

Life began for Walter Reed on September 13, 1851, in a cabin at Belroi, Gloucester County, Virginia.

He had often joked that, right from the start, he had been under a wandering star. His father, Lemuel Sutton Reed, was a Methodist preacher who carried the Word to the scattered villages and farms of North Carolina and Virginia. Even the cabin of his birth was nothing more than a temporary shelter.

A few weeks before Walter's birth, Lemuel Reed had been transferred from Murfreesboro, North Carolina, to Belroi. It was a move that Lemuel and his wife, Pharaba, made happily, for Belroi boasted a fine parsonage, just the place to bring a new son or daughter into the world. Unfortunately, by the time they arrived in the parish, the fine parsonage had burned to the ground a few days earlier.

Their parishioners, however, had appealed to the owner of a nearby Belroi plantation for some sort of comfortable accomodations. There were four children in the Reed family already, and Pharaba was expecting her fifth child soon. The plantation owner, Mr. Stubbs, readily agreed to make the cabin of his overseer available to the family.

It was in this small cabin, when Indian summer was on the land, that Walter Reed was born.

He grew to be a good looking child, fair-haired and blue-eyed, slender and short, one of those youngsters who never look big enough for their age. By nature, he was quiet, even tempered, and sensitive to the feelings of others.

Before he was five years old, Walter understood that the family world was made up of daily household chores and that everyone, regardless of size, had to lend a hand with them. He learned to tote water and firewood, to wash and dry dishes and to sweep down a floor. His diminutive, energetic mother soon had him helping her tend the flower and vegetable garden that she established wherever the family lived.

By the time Walter entered school, he had lived in five houses. Several weeks after his birth, the Reeds moved into the newly built parsonage at Belroi. Within two years, Lemuel was transferred to Princess Anne County. He spent two years there, then two at Murfreesboro, North Carolina, and two at Farmville in Prince Edward County.

Walter entered school at Farmville in the autumn of 1857. Mrs. Booker, his first teacher, handed him a copy of

[*45*]

McGuffey's *First Eclectic Reader* and a small black easel on which to do sums.

He was a good student from this first school day on. Curiosity and the desire to learn were natural to him, as they were to all the Reeds. He made a fine academic record at Farmville and at all the other Virginia schools he attended.

By 1860, it seemed to the nine-year-old boy that his parents and their friends could speak of nothing else but the unrest between the North and the South. Lemuel Reed said darkly that, should Lincoln be elected President, many Southern states would leave the Union and form a nation of their own. There would be war.

Lemuel's prediction came true. Upon Lincoln's election in November, Walter added a new word to his vocabulary— secession. In the next few months, 11 southern states, among them Virginia, dropped from the Union, and Walter found himself living in a new nation, the Confederated States of America. In 1861, the Confederacy fired upon Fort Sumter, and the Civil War began. Jim, the oldest of the four Reed boys, enlisted in General Robert E. Lee's army and marched away to Richmond, the capital of the Confederacy.

The end of the war came in the spring of 1865. Slowly, and as efficiently as was possible in a wrecked land, the Reeds got back to a normal life. Lemuel won an appointment as presiding elder of the Charlottesville district, enabling him to enroll Walter and Chris in Charlottesville Institute to prepare for their entry into the University of Virginia. Jim, his left arm lost at the battle of Antietam, was already at the University, along with Tom. Lemuel was far from being a rich man, but he was determined to see his sons through college. To provide them with the finest schooling possible was a point of honor with him.

The world looked bright to the Reeds as 1865 came to an end. Walter ranked near the head of his class and loved his work at Charlottesville Institute. Lemuel was delighted with his new position; Pharaba was filled with wonder at the spaciousness of the home that went with it. The family agreed that Christmas that year was the finest they had ever celebrated. For the first time in four years, all the boys were safe at home. Pharaba wept with joy when she saw them seated together at the dinner table.

Just two months later, in February of 1866, the always frail little Pharaba died suddenly. Lemuel went about his work blindly, automatically. Jim, with the hardness of the army still in him, quietly cursed a fate that shattered a family so soon after it had been reunited. For the first time in his life, Walter could neither concentrate on his studies or take pleasure from them. Many months passed before the wound left by his mother's death healed.

He completed his studies at Charlottesville Institute in the early summer of 1867 and turned his thoughts eagerly to the University of Virginia. He had heard Jim and Tom tell wonderous tales of the school, and he could hardly wait until he was a part of it. Adding to his impatience was the fact that he knew exactly what goal he would seek once he was enrolled there.

Like all boys, he had had his share of passing ambitions. But one had remained with him, and he knew that it would be with him all his life. Perhaps because of all the suffering he had seen in the war, perhaps because as his father's son he was filled with an urge to help others, but for whatever reason, he knew in his heart that he wanted to be a doctor.

The University of Virginia, with one of the most respected medical schools in the nation, was the doorway to the realization of that ambition. Very shortly after he had been accepted by the University, Walter came to look back on his earlier schooling as child's play.

Reed drove himself mercilessly at his studies. He was determined to attain the highest academic standing possible. At the end of the term, he planned to seek permission to enter the School of Medicine a year ahead of schedule and to earn his medical degree in just nine months, provided that he could pass the school's final examination at the end of that period.

It was an unusual request, but one that was sometimes granted in cases of emergency. Walter felt that he was such a case. He had seen that Lemuel was clearly suffering under the burden of keeping four sons in college; he wanted to do whatever he could to shorten the time that he would be a part of that burden. Lemuel had married the widowed Mrs. Mary Kyle Byrd of Harrisburg, Virginia, and at the moment was awaiting the arrival of their first child.

Walter presented his request to the university medical board early in the summer. As he had expected, the members were shocked and amused. Sixteen years old and he wanted a medical degree! Ridiculous! Did not young Reed understand that the courses in medicine were among the most difficult the university had to offer? Did he not understand that it was almost impossible for any student—much

The medical board was shocked by young Walter Reed's request.

less a 16-year-old boy—to win a doctor's degree in nine short months?

Walter understood fully. He glanced at board member Dr. John Staige Davis, professor of anatomy. He reminded the board that Dr. Davis had taken his medical degree at the tender age of 17. "I merely wish to see if I can duplicate that feat," he said.

A ripple of laughter passed through the assembled doctors. All right, Mr. Reed would have his chance.

The demands of the medical school were so great that Walter had time for nothing but study. He attended classes and worked in the laboratories from dawn until well after dark. Then, eyes burning, he sat in his room until long past midnight studying. Lemuel fretted about his son's health. Jim and Tom told the minister to stop worrying. Walter never looked better in his life. He was young and hard work agreed with him.

The nine months at medical school passed in a haze for the boy. Walter was no more than dimly conscious of political corruption flowering in the wake of war, and the Ku Klux Klan launching their rides of terror. All that mattered to him was that his final examination day was bearing down on him with an amazing speed. Finally, in June, 1869, dead tired, but confident, he sat down to that test. Soon afterward he was notified that, at 17, he had won his medical degree.

Many would have considered it an accomplishment calling for a good rest. But to Walter, it marked the start of renewed effort. Immediately upon his graduation, he enrolled in the school of medicine attached to New York's Belle-vue Hospital. The University of Virginia did not have hospital facilities, depriving its students of valuable training in clinical work, and it was the custom of graduates to take a second medical degree from a New York or Philadelphia hospital.

Walter received his second M.D. degree at Bellevue in 1870 and interned at Kings County Hospital, Brooklyn. During the days, he attended lectures, assisted physicians in the hospital clinic, and performed autopsies. On weekends, he scoured New York from one end to the other, finding it a place of never-fading wonder. He visited the opera, the museums, Central Park, and the about-to-be-completed St. Patrick's Cathedral.

He also saw the poor sections of the city—the endless, crowded tenement districts where people lived and died in filth and poverty and hunger. The sights in these miserable neighborhoods touched him deeply; they brought to the forefront of his being his desire to help those in need. In 1873, just turning 22, Walter Reed accepted the post of health inspector for New York's tenement districts. He later worked for the Board of Health in Brooklyn.

The practical experience he gained proved invaluable. His clinical work presented him with an endless variety of illnesses, many of them in advanced stages because ignorance and fear had kept their victims from treatment for too long. Tours of his districts acquainted him thoroughly with sanitation problems. He learned to deal with sickness where he found it.

But, after a time, the work began to discourage him. He was performing fine service, he knew, but he was not building up his private practice for the future. He had reached the point of life where he wanted to settle down. He told his friends that he wanted nothing more than to find a small town in which to settle and develop a practice.

Then, suddenly and unexpectedly, he took a step that seemed contrary to all his desires. He applied for and won, on the basis of an examination, a commission in the United States Army Medical Corps. His reasons for this step were quite simple. The Army would give him an assured income, part of which could be saved for the day when he returned to private practice. And, no matter how much he talked of settling down, he still had a hankering to see something of the country. He planned to remain in the service four years.

Soon after he pinned his lieutenant's bars to his shoulders, he surprised his friends further by taking a bride. She was the lovely Emilie Lawrence of Murfreesboro, North Carolina. They had met while he was vacationing in that city, and they had corresponded for close to a year.

Lieutenant Reed and Emilie Lawrence were married on April 25, 1876, at Murfreesboro. They spent their honeymoon in the Shenandoah Valley. Then they packed their trunks and valises, and headed west. Walter's first service for the United States Army was in the heat and dust of Arizona, first at Fort Lowell and then at Camp Apache.

It was good that Walter and Emilie had an adventurous streak in them, for life at Lowell and Apache was anything but comfortable. The weather was blistering hot in the summer and icy cold in the winter. Dust boiled in off the desert daily. The posts were in the heart of Apache country. Even though the Indians and white men had been at peace for several years, there was the constant danger that trouble would break out again.

Army life, however, had its compensations. The officers' families were a close knit group, depending on each other for companionship and entertainment. Picnics, dances, and song fests were the order of the day, any day of the week. The people that Walter and Emilie met fascinated them; there were tough old Army regulars, weatherbeaten men who had passed most of their days in a series of rugged outposts; there were hard-drinking, hard-talking mule skinners; there were leathery skinned Apaches now working as scouts for the Army; there were Mexican cooks with their frantic babble and their exotic foods; there were West Point trained officers, reserved and impeccable in speech and behavior; there were young doctors new to the Medical Corps, improvising facilities in the midst of nowhere. Walter and Emilie agreed that they could not have chosen a more exciting life. At Camp Apache Emilie gave birth to their first child, a boy. The new Reed arrived on December 4, 1877. His parents named him Walter Lawrence.

The family of three returned to the East Coast in 1880, and Walter was promoted to the rank of captain. By now, with three years of service life behind him, he had discarded his plan to leave the Army and set himself up in private practice. He liked the work he was doing too well to abandon it, and he felt that he was in a branch of medicine that greatly needed his services. The Medical Corps was the least prosperous of the service organizations. Equipment—what there was of it—was old, and appropriations for new were scant. Hospitals were poorly constructed, designed to last ten years at the most. There were too few men in the Corps to care for far too many soldiers. There were no women nurses in the service yet. But there were brilliant doctors, doctors who were fighting to better conditions.

For a few months in 1880, he was stationed at Fort McHenry, near Baltimore. Then came a tour of duty in Nebraska, first at Fort Omaha and then at Fort Sidney close to the western border of the state. While they were living at Fort Omaha, Walter and Emilie had a second child born to them, a daughter whom they named Emilie Lawrence, but whom they always called Blossom.

Ten years passed before Walter and his growing family returned to Baltimore. Captain Reed was now 39 years old, an experienced officer with a sweeping mustache and hair gone gray at the temples. He was still slender, wiry and hard muscled, having lived for years in rugged garrisons. His speech was as soft as ever—though it could turn to steel when necessary—and his nature was as gentle as it had been the day he had married Emilie. Outwardly, he was good-natured, the possessor of an excellent sense of humor. Inwardly, he was troubled. He had worked hard to improve hospital conditions on the posts to which he had been assigned, and in many instances he had succeeded. But he had been a captain for ten years now. He felt that he was lost among the many men in the Corps.

In 1890, upon his return to Baltimore, he determined to rid himself of that lost feeling. He applied to Surgeon General Charles Sutherland for permission to perform bacteriological research under Dr. William Henry Welch at nearby Johns Hopkins Hospital. Sutherland approved his request.

From the beginning, the work in Welch's laboratory

fascinated him. He studied bacteriology and pathology, mastering them quickly. Before long, he was embarked on a study of his own, a study involving a disease that had always interested him, typhoid fever.

Throughout his career, whenever he had performed an autopsy on a typhoid fever victim, he had noticed the presence of little lumps on the lymph glands of the liver. Those lumps always baffled him. What were they? Where did they come from? What caused them? Those questions no doctor of the day could answer. In Welch's laboratory, he set about to find the answers. In a series of experiments, in which he induced typhoid in a number of laboratory animals, he established the fact that the lumps originated as small groups of dead liver cells.

Thrilled with his accomplishment, Reed turned to other investigations. He looked into the contagiousness of erysipelas and, in March, 1892, published a paper on it in the *Boston Medical and Surgical Journal*. The paper—his first attempt at scientific writing—secured him a reputation as one of the leading bacteriologists in the Medical Corps.

Reed's work caught the eye of General George Miller Sternberg, the most famous scientist in the Corps. A bacteriologist himself, Sternberg had produced the first textbook ever written on the subject in the United States. Sternberg had an idea that he would be able to put Reed to use one day soon.

That day came the very next year. In the spring of 1893, Sternberg was appointed Surgeon General, replacing General Sutherland. Sternberg immediately established the Army Medical School at Washington, D.C. He selected Captain

Walter Reed to be professor of bacteriology. Reed now carried the rank of major.

All the while that Reed had been conducting his investigations, he had been distracted by miscellaneous military duties and by transfers to several eastern garrisons. Such annoyances were now at an end. He could devote all his time to teaching and research in bacteriology. And, for the first time in their married life, he and Emilie could settle down in one place for a reasonable length of time.

Major and Mrs. Reed settled on Cooke Avenue, in the Georgetown area of Washington. The new professor happily threw himself into his work. He spent his days lecturing to his classes. All his free hours were given to his laboratory. With Dr. James Carroll, his assistant, he continued his researches into typhoid fever and erysipelas, adding investigations into pneumonia, malaria, and abdominal typhus. His writings on these subjects in various scientific journals of the day won him a national reputation.

April 25, 1898, marked the end of the contented, settled years for the Reed family. On that day, the United States formally declared a state of war with Spain. Since 1895, the people of Cuba had been in revolt against the oppressive rule of Spain. For three years, United States attempts to arbitrate the conflict had failed. A wave of sympathy for Cuba had swept the United States, mounting to fever pitch by 1898. It had been climaxed on February 15, when the U.S. battleship *Maine*, anchored in Havana harbor to protect U.S. business interests in Cuba was destroyed by a mysterious explosion. Though the explosion may have been accidental, large segments of the U.S. public, press, and government held Spain responsible for the disaster. The result was war.

Army authorities were faced with a chilling set of statistics having nothing to do with battles. According to the present death rate, the following months would see more than 5,000 soldiers dead of contagious disease in crowded foreign and U.S. camps.

The principal killers were typhoid fever and yellow jack. Reed first fretted at the Army Medical College, watching his son enlist and ship out to the Caribbean. At last Reed was sent into the field. In August, he was asked to head a board to investigate the spread of typhoid fever and formulate a method for its prevention.

At that time, the disease was a bafflling one. Doctors knew that its causal agent was a germ called Eberth's bacillus, but they were uncertain as to the manner in which it was spread. Reed, accompanied by Drs. Victor C. Vaughan and Edward O. Shakespeare, visited a string of typhoid ridden camps in the Southern states. The three doctors came up with a firm definition of the disease and established the fact that Eberth's bacillus is mainly spread by flies that congregate around poorly maintained sanitary facilities.

Reed returned to Washington to write a report on his board's findings. But, before he had a chance to get to do so, Sternberg put him and Carroll to work investigating Sanarelli's bacillus of yellow jack.

Very soon afterwards Sternberg had called him to his office and had put him in charge of the Yellow Fever Commission.

Reed stirred uncomfortably in the rocker and opened

his eyes. He sat for a moment, uncertain of where he was. He pulled himself to his feet and stared out the window. The veranda below him was silent, the hospital in darkness, except for a glowing lamp here and there in an office window. Without looking at his watch, he knew that midnight had come and gone and that he had been asleep for more than three hours.

He moved to his bedroom and dropped on his steel cot. In just a few hours, he would launch the attack against the fever. He would work carefully, first isolating and identifying the germ of yellow jack. It was the right and proper way to begin the job.

Or was it?

He stared up at the ceiling. Jesse Lazear's hard words of doubt were in his mind. The memory of them stung him deeply.

Chapter 5

The Battle Begins

Reed awoke early in the morning of June 26th, refreshed, ready for work, and filled with hopes for the future. Twenty-one days later, all those hopes lay shattered at his feet.

During the last week in June and the first two weeks in July, he and his three doctors searched night and day for some sign of the bacillus icteroide. Eighteen vicious cases of yellow fever passed through the laboratories at Camp Columbia and Hospital Number One; four victims died. The doctors probed each case with a patience that slowly withered with the passing days. Agramonte efficiently and quietly performed his autopsies, and found nothing. Reed, Lazear, and Carroll daily took blood samples from the living and intestinal tissue from the dead, and subjected the specimens to careful miscroscopic study, earning nothing for their efforts but burning eyes and shelves littered with sample slides.

The bacillus icteroide, or whatever germ was responsible for yellow fever, refused to show itself. No one microbe was common among the victims, living or dead.

The epidemic at Havana and Quemados worsened. Dr. Roger Post Ames, who had always had such good luck in the treatment of the fever, privately confessed to Reed that he could do nothing but stand by and watch his patients die. Major William Crawford Gorgas enforced the strictest sanitary measures in both Havana and Quemados. On the theory that disease can not long survive in the midst of cleanliness, he had his men clean the streets, cart off piles of rubbish, and mop up pools of stagnant water. Such measures had helped in earlier epidemics of malaria, but they did no good against the yellow jack. Cubans living in Quemados told Reed that it was the worst epidemic within living memory. They stared hopelessly out at the sea beyond Camp Columbia, and they died by the hundreds. The epidemic spread to the distant city of Santa Clara.

A feeling of helplessness surged over the men in Lazear's laboratory. They worked farther and farther into the night, sometimes looking up from their microscopes to find the eastern sky yellow with the dawn. They checked and re-checked every specimen. They prayed for some break. One afternoon Carroll shoved his notebook aside and dropped his forehead into the palm of one hand. His bald head was coated with perspiration.

"Is it possible," he muttered, "that we're looking for something that can't be seen? Is it possible that it's invisible to the human eye, even with the help of a microscope?"

To add to Reed's worries during those terrible three weeks, there was Jesse Lazear. The young doctor went about his assignments with his customary thoroughness and drive; he was too good a doctor to let his personal feelings interfere with the perfection of his work. But he was completely disgusted with all that was being done. Reed could tell by the way Lazear softly cursed at his microscope when it failed to show him what he was looking for. There was the sound of anger in the raw scratching of Jesse's pen as he scribbled down his latest failures in his notebook. Near the end of June, Jesse shoved aside his work and, his eyes blazing and head thrust forward, came to Reed with a plea. "Please try the mosquito theory, Major. Before it's too late. Get us out of this blind alley."

"Jesse, we can't go running off in another direction at this time. We've got to keep after the icteroide. There may be some flaw in our search methods, some flaw that we may uncover any day now. Just because we can't see the icteroide today doesn't mean that we won't see it tomorrow."

"Or the day after that, or the day after, or never!" Lazear said. He shook his head vigorously. His face was ashen and haggard. "No. No, Major. You're so wrong. Get away from this line of research completely. It's a waste of time."

Reed himself was close to exhaustion. "Jesse, please . . . ."

"Major, I know what I'm talking about. Listen to me, please. Several weeks ago, I was called upon to treat the first fever case this year at Quemados. The patient lived at 20 General Lee Street. Two weeks later, the second case appeared in town, just around the corner, at 102 Calzada Real. Now listen, Major. The people in those houses had not had any contact whatsoever with each other. They'd never visited each other; they'd never passed each other on the street;

they'd never even been introduced. Yet the disease got from one house to the other, the disease that is supposed to be transmitted through personal contact with the fomites. How did it travel between those two houses? How, Major? In only one way. Its germs were carried from one address to another by an insect."

"If that's true—and I'm not saying that it is—then there are thousands of insects that we must look at in this island. We'd be forever and a day checking them all."

"Start with the mosquito!"

Reed slapped the table, his eyes flashing in a rare burst of anger. "No, Jesse! You criticize the fomites theory, and yet you push forward another theory that has failed just as often in laboratory experiments. You know full well that Finlay has never been able to produce one single case of yellow fever from a mosquito. That's true, isn't it? Well, isn't it?"

Reluctantly, angrily, Lazear nodded.

"Then," Reed said flatly, "don't bother me with it again."

Lazear stared at him coldly for a moment. A biting answer came up to the young doctor's lips, but he held it back. "I can't promise that, Major, and you know it. Perhaps you'll let me come back to fight another day."

Reed smiled. He shrugged helplessly.

"I don't think I could stop you if I wanted to."

Two weeks later Jesse cornered Reed with a question. "Major, have you kept track of the health of the doctors and nurses here and at Hospital Number One?"

"Of course."

"How many have fallen ill?"

Reed knew a trap when he saw one. He sighed. Lazear beat him to the answer.

"Not one. Right?"

Reed nodded reluctantly.

Lazear grinned. "Strange isn't it? Particularly when they've been tending patients and handling fomites in their bedding, bedding that should be absolutely loaded. Now, why don't we go after the mosquito. If we find that it causes the fever, then we can figure a method to wipe it out and get rid of the fever. Then we can take our time about finding the germ that causes the disease. The important thing is that the fever will be done for."

He spun on his heel and walked away, leaving Reed to think it over. Reed did just that. But he did nothing about it. All his energies were concentrated on the icteroide. And old beliefs, after all, die slow and hard.

On July 18, Lazear was back. This time, he carried a medical journal, open to a page toward the middle. He slipped the journal down on Reed's work table and pointed at it triumphantly.

"You must see this, Major."

"What is it?"

"An article by Dr. Henry H. Carter of the Marine Hospital Service. He has been studying the yellow fever problem for years."

Reed wearily pushed his work aside. "And he's undoubtedly found something to support your mosquito theory."

"I think so. But first let me give you a little background information," Lazear said. "As you know, malaria requires a definite length of time to appear in a person. When Dr.

Donald Ross—you remember I mentioned him at the first meeting of the Commission—when he discovered that the *Anopheles* mosquito carries malaria, he found something else."

Lazear's forefinger tapped the work table to emphasize his point. "He found that the mosquito, after it had sucked the blood from a malaria victim, was incapable of passing the disease to another person for a number of days. During that time, the microbes of malaria were growing strong inside it. Only when those germs were strong enough could the mosquito pass malaria along to healthy persons through its bite."

Reed nodded, "I've heard that the same thing was shown in the mosquito carrying filaria, and the tick responsible for Texas cattle fever."

"True," Lazear said. His tired eyes glowed with excitement. He leaned far forward, his face close to Reed's. "And now we come back to Dr. Carter. He noticed it took from two to three weeks for the first case of yellow fever in an area to produce the second case. After that, people fell sick within a week. Doesn't it seem possible that two to three weeks pass between the first and second cases of fever in an area because the germs of yellow jack—like those of malaria—are growing in strength inside an insect? Doesn't it seem reasonable, Major?"

Reed was saved from answering by the appearance of Captain A. N. Stark, chief surgeon of the Quemados area. He brought bad news. The strange illness that had struck early in the month at Pinar del Rio, the capital of Cuba's westernmost province, was still raging unabated. The number of American deaths was on the increase. The camp commandant there said that his medical officer insisted that the illness was pernicious malarial fever.

"But I don't trust that doctor, Reed. I don't trust him at all," Stark said. "I'd like to send one of your men up there to have a look around."

Agramonte was the natural choice, for he was presumed to be immune. He arrived at Pinal del Rio the next afternoon and examined the patients in the tent hospital. He was convinced that the diagnosis of pernicious malarial fever was sheer nonsense. An autopsy on the body of a soldier who had died that morning removed all doubt; the condition of the man's stomach and intestinal tract meant but one thing, yellow fever.

Agramonte went directly to the camp commander. The commander, a burly, cigar smoking man, heard him out and then said flatly that he did not think the young doctor knew what he was talking about. His medical officer had diagnosed the illness as pernicious malarial fever, and that was good enough for him. He had no doubt that a goodly share of his men were pretending to be sicker than was actually the case; they were lazy louts and were probably trying to avoid their rightful share of camp duty.

In icy, clipped tones Agramonte replied that the men were seriously ill. Furthermore he said, the camp's medical officer was unfit to wear the uniform of the Medical Corps or to be addressed as "Doctor."

"He's under the influence of narcotics and has been for a long while. You know that to be the truth, don't you?" Agramonte asked.

The commander shrugged. Yes, he knew. But what could he do?

Ignoring his visitor's rage, the commander refused to acknowledge any of Agramonte's suggestions for the protection of the camp. No, he would not establish a quarantine ward for the sick, nor would he move those of his 900 men who were still healthy to an airy grove of trees north of the camp. He did not believe in pampering troops. Let them contract the pernicious malarial fever and get it out of their systems. That was the best way to handle the whole situation.

And he certainly would not trade his spacious, open quarters for the primitive confines of a tent in a grove of trees. Fifteen years of life in the service had taught him one lesson: comfort is a hard thing to come by.

"Is that your final decision?" Agramonte asked. His voice was choked. He needed all his will power to keep from hitting the officer full in the face.

"It is."

"Then," Agramonte said stiffly, "perhaps you'll be kind enough to direct me to the camp telegraph office."

The officer shrugged carelessly. "Sure, Doc, anything to help. Out that door and straight ahead."

Agramonte's last glimpse of the officer revealed him calmly lighting a new cigar.

At sunset, Reed strode into Captain A. N. Stark's headquarters at Camp Columbia. His cheeks were flushed in anger as he swept past an orderly's desk without a word and pushed Stark's door open.

[66]

"Agramonte's in trouble," he said.

Stark looked up from a report that he was writing, his eyes narrowing when he saw Reed's expression. He could not remember a time when the Major's face had been so stiff and hard.

"What is it?" Stark asked.

In reply, Reed handed him the telegram from Agramonte that so vividly described the sorry situation at Pinar del Rio. Stark's eyes ran over the terse words and his own face went white. He shoved his work aside and grabbed pen and paper.

Reed watched him scribble the first of two messages intended for Pinar del Rio. He addressed it to the camp commander and told him in no uncertain terms that he was under orders from a representative of General Leonard Wood to do whatever Agramonte told him to do. If the commander did not cooperate, he faced a court martial. He was also instructed to dismiss his medical officer and send him back to Havana immediately.

"He'll never do another bit of harm if I have anything to say about it," Stark muttered.

The second message authorized Agramonte to set up special fever wards immediately. He was to put those wards under the strictest quarantine. He was to assign men, preferably those who had been rendered immune by earlier attacks, to clean the camp from one end to the other. All healthy troops were to be moved to a safe area. Any help or supplies that he needed would be available from Camp Columbia. Nurses would arrive on the morning train.

Stark's pen stopped, and the chief surgeon glanced up

at Reed. "I'm sending you to help him. Right?"

"Very right, Captain. I was going, whether you suggested it or not."

Reed, hot and tired after a long train ride, arrived at Pinar del Rio early in the afternoon of July 21 and found that Agramonte had the camp well under control. His face flushed with triumph, Agramonte showed Reed the fever wards—tents with their side flaps up—that he had established.

"They're roped off from the rest of the camp. They're under constant guard. No one can get in or out."

He said that he had put former fever cases to work as nurses until Stark's promised detachment arrived. He escorted Reed to a wooded area at the north end of the camp. Tents for 900 men were pitched there, and Reed could not mistake the joy in Agramonte's tone when the young doctor said:

"The commander's tent is out there in the middle."

"Good." Reed's heavy mustache twitched with pleasure. He regarded Agramonte thoughtfully for a long moment. "I should think that he'll have to stay there for quite a time, wouldn't you, Doctor. My guess is that the danger of the epidemic is going to be slow in passing."

Agramonte's smile broadened. He tried to nod gravely, but he couldn't quite bring it off. "Oh, yes, Doctor, very, very slow."

Agramonte's smile faded quickly, replaced by a deep frown, when he informed Reed that the camp medical officer had been placed on the morning train for Havana. It was a crime that helpless men should have been at the mercy of his ignorance and weakness. Perhaps some now sick or dead would have been still quite healthy if the doctor had recognized the disease for what it was when he had first seen it.

Reed and Agramonte immediately got down to their most pressing work, discovering how the epidemic had started. Some clue of its birth might set them on the trail to its death. Their efforts had been in vain at Havana and Quemados. Perhaps their luck would be better here.

First, they went painstakingly back over all the medical reports of the past weeks. Then they went into the fever wards and out into the grove of trees where the still healthy soldiers were to be found, and they asked questions. The questions were always the same.

Did the men remember anything special that had happened just before the outbreak?

Had anyone from the other fever areas, Havana or Quemados, visited the camp? Had anyone from the camp gone on leave to Havana or Quemados? How long after the appearance of the first case did the second case appear? What were the camp sanitary measures at the time of the outbreak?

The answers were enough to drive a man mad. "The fact is, Doctor, everything was just fine until suddenly—out of a clear blue sky—one man was ill, complaining of a backache and a headache. And then he was vomiting and turning yellow in the face. And then the other men were falling ill. And then there was death."

The fomites theory was dying. Not one of the things Reed had seen or heard here at Pinar del Rio supported that long revered belief. Together with all the things he had seen and heard at Havana and Quemados, the theory was being crushed to absurdity.

[69]

None of the orderlies or the nurses showed any signs of the fever, yet all of them had worked for weeks in the wards at Camp Columbia. The nurse who had held Private Thompson's head at the last stage of the disease was here in Pinar del Rio. Her face was ashen with fatigue, but she was not ill.

Reed looked into the barracks from which several fatal cases had been carried. Hundreds of men had continued to live there right up to the moment that Agramonte had put his safety measures into effect. The illness had not spread to them.

Reed walked to the tent that he and Agramonte shared at the edge of the quarantine area. Agramonte was seated at a camp table, his dark brows knitted as he studied a medical report. Reed sat down on the edge of his cot. He put his face in his hands for a long moment and massaged his eyes with the tips of his fingers.

"It's no good, is it?"

Agramonte had watched his superior officer closely these past days, and he knew what was in Reed's mind.

"The fomites theory?"

"Yes. It's no good, is it?"

Agramonte shrugged. His heart went out to the older man. Reed looked exhausted. There were hollows in the flesh beneath his high, knobbed cheekbones. "I don't know."

"It can't be any good. All the evidence points to the fact that it's nonsense. If the fomites theory were true, then the fever would spread uniformly among all the men who came in contact with a patient. But it doesn't. It hops about." He banged a fist into the palm of his open hand. "It hops about like—like a—"

"Mosquito?"

"Yes! Like a mosquito."

Agramonte picked up the report he had been studying when Reed came into the tent, and handed it across to the cot.

"Here," he said. "Read this. It will trouble you all the more."

Reed's eyes started wearily down the first page of the report. Then his brows arched and his back straightened. He glanced up at Agramonte and then went back to the page. He realized that what he was reading was the last blow the fomites theory could take.

The report stated that a young private had been confined to the camp's one-room guardhouse with eight other prisoners since June 6. They had been under constant guard all during the time that the epidemic was first attacking the camp. None of them had left the prison area; not one of them had ever been given the chance to come in contact with the fever. Yet, on June 12, the young private had fallen ill with nausea. Six days later, he was dead. Not one of his fellow prisoners and not one of the soldiers guarding him had fallen ill with the fever. Not even the prisoner who later stated that he was sleeping in the very bunk in which the young private had died, and under the very same blankets!

Reed stared up at Agramonte. Reed's eyes were tired and expressionless. He tapped the report with the back of his hand.

"I'm going back to Quemados in the morning," he said. "I must talk with Lazear."

"You're going to look into Finlay's mosquito idea?"

Reed nodded. "The fever is spread by some sort of insect that crawls or flies. It could be anyone of thousands of bugs coming out of the jungles in this island. "We'll start with Finlay's mosquitoes. At least there's been some work done in that area."

Agramonte was silent, thoughtful for a moment. "You know that Finlay's every attempt to prove the mosquito idea has failed?"

"Yes."

"Failed because not once in hundreds of tries was he able to succeed in having one of his infected mosquitoes pass the disease on to a laboratory animal?"

"Yes."

Agramonte asked, "You know then the decision that you must make?"

"I do."

The wagon dropped Reed and his baggage off in front of the officer's club at Camp Columbia. An orderly carried his luggage in. Reed smoothed his tunic and prepared to cross over to Lazear's laboratory.

Reed was weary and covered with perspiration. He had ridden the whole day in a shower of coal dust from the engine of the rickety train. He needed and much wanted a bath. But he dared not delay meeting with Lazear. He might as well get Lazear's grinning face out of the way as soon as possible.

He slowly crossed the hospital grounds, coming at last to the steps leading up to Lazear's laboratory. He stopped. Hard in his mind was the decision that Agramonte had mentioned yesterday. It was a decision that had kept him awake all last night.

Suddenly, almost without willing it, he walked away from the laboratory. He couldn't face Lazear just yet. He had to have time to find if he were justified in making the decision which faced him.

He did not pay much attention where his footsteps carried him, but he was not surprised when he felt wood planking underfoot. He had come out on the footbridge spanning the gulley that separated the main hospital from the isolation wards. Here he had paused to think on his first day at Camp Columbia. As he had done that first day, he took off his cap and felt the cool breeze from the sea stir through his hair. He leaned his elbows on the rail of the bridge and stared down at the railroad tracks below.

Hardly more than a month had passed since his first day in Cuba. He passed his hand across his forehead. It seemed more like a century.

The decision he faced sprang directly from a problem that had faced Finlay for 19 years. Finlay had always needed to succeed in one experiment in order to silence his critics and prove his theory. He had needed to produce a case of yellow fever in a laboratory animal by infecting that animal with the bite of the mosquito. But not once had he succeeded. There were four possible reasons for the failures. Reed told himself as he stared down a the railroad tracks.

First, the mosquito was not the carrier of yellow fever. This was as far as the medical profession had gone in its thinking.

Second, Finlay might have been guilty of some error, some carelessness, in the way he performed the experiment. Reed dismissed this possibility immediately. He had heard that Finlay was a man much too fussy for carelessness. And the old man had repeated the experiment far too many times in the past 19 years not to have discovered an error in his methods.

Third, the laboratory animals that Finlay had used might not have been susceptible to the fever. Perhaps nature had equipped them with a built-in immunity. Nature was always performing strange tricks like that.

Or—and this fourth possibility chilled Reed's heart—perhaps nature had equipped all animals with an immunity to yellow fever. There were some indications that this might well be the case. Reed knew that Finlay had used every type of animal conceivable—monkeys, rats, mice, rabbits, and guinea pigs. And he knew, too, that just recently Agramonte had tried, and failed, to induce the fever into several laboratory animals by directly injecting them with the blood of fever victims.

Without the experiment, the theory could never be proved. But, if all animals were immune to yellow fever, then how could a scientist ever perform the experiment? What sort of creature could he use? What creature was there that was definitely susceptible to the disease?

The answer was horribly clear.

A man.

And now Reed was face-to-face with the decision that he must make.

Was it not murder to deliberately inject the germs of a filthy disease into a man?

Reed knew himself for what he was. He knew he did not really have the raw physical courage that it took to win medals in battle. He was quiet and, according to his wife, gentle of nature. He had joined the Army to ease suffering, not to create it. And now he was faced with the very same possibility that a soldier in the field had to face; he was up against the possibility of killing another human being.

Horrible thoughts poured through his mind. He saw himself putting a mosquito with the venom of yellow jack in it to the arm of a man. He saw the man grow sick. He saw the face turn yellow and the flesh waste away. He saw the bleeding gums. He saw the black vomit. He saw the man die.

Then, as suddenly as they had come, these thoughts fell away. In their place came memories of all the sights he had seen since his arrival in Cuba. He saw again all the rows of yellowed faces here at Columbia and Havana and at Pinar del Rio.

As a doctor, he had to fight with every weapon at his command. The experiment was a weapon. It had to be used, even if it ended in death, even if the doctor in charge was called a murderer, even if his career was shattered when an outraged public learned of what he had done.

Reed found that he had walked to the end of the bridge. He stopped. A happy thought came suddenly to mind. The human being who submitted himself to the experiment need not die. He would have the best of medical care. The Yellow Fever Commission would see to that. The doctors of the Commission would stay with him day and night, giving him the best medical care possible, literally pulling him back to health by the strength of their combined will power.

With an odd sense of lightness, he walked across the

[75]

hospital grounds and into the laboratory where Lazear was bending over a microscope.

"Jesse."

Lazear looked up. Pleasure and surprise came into his face. He jumped to his feet and grasped Reed's hand.

"Major! We didn't expect you for another week. How is Agramonte?"

"Fine," Reed said. "And now I have something unexpected to tell you. I want you to do me a favor."

"Yes?" Lazear stared narrowly at his superior officer. Reed's manner was buoyant, but his face was dead white.

"I want you to make an appointment for us to see Carlos Finlay."

Lazear's mouth dropped open. He blinked, as if he could not believe what he had heard.

"Are you serious?"

"I've never been more serious in my life."

Lazear sat down. He leaned far back, closing his eyes. He murmured, "Thank God. Thank God."

Chapter 6

A Mosquito Called *Culex Fasciatus*

Dr. Carlos Juan Finlay was 67 years old, a small, bent man with a pink, puckered face, white hair, and gigantic side whiskers. He wore steel rimmed spectacles, round as silver dollars. Finlay had been born in Cuba, of a Scottish father and a French mother, and educated in Germany, France, Havana and the United States. Nineteen years earlier, in February of 1881, he had announced to the International Sanitary Conference at Washington his belief that a foreign agent spreads the germ of yellow jack. In August, he identified the agent as a mosquito, *Culex fasciatus*. From that day, he had been called "the mosquito man." It was a tender point with him.

His stucco home, surrounded by high walls, was on the outskirts of Havana. He was delighted to welcome three visitors from the U.S. Army Medical Corps. He led Reed, Lazear, and Carroll into his very cool and very neat living room, thinking they had come for a pleasant afternoon chat. The old man's attitude changed when Reed explained the true purpose of the visit. The three doctors wished to discuss his mosquito theory, did they? Were they acquainted with the medical profession's opinion of that theory?

"We are, sir," Reed said.

"Then am I to assume that you have come here to make sport of it?" the old man asked tartly. He was leaning forward in his chair now, ready to thrust himself up and show his guests the door.

"No, sir you are not."

"It's happened before, you know. I have no intention of turning my house into a circus for the skeptical."

Reed assured him that they had come on serious business. He explained that observations at Havana, Quemados, and, more recently, Pinar del Rio, had led the Yellow Fever Commission to suspect that the fever was spread by some sort of insect.

Finlay's expression, as Reed talked, went from anger and doubt to sheer joy. Reed half expected him to bounce up and down on the stuffed chair and clap his hands.

Reed put up a warning hand. "A moment, please, Doctor. I said we suspect an insect, not necessarily a mosquito. We wish to start with an investigation of your theory because so much work has been done on it."

"Of course. Of course, gentlemen," Finlay said. He was wringing his hands with excitement. Lazear and Carroll exchanged glances and smiled. "But you won't have to search further. My theory will prove itself out. I know it will."

Reed hoped with all his heart that it would. The old

man was almost pathetic in his joy. Nineteen years is a long time to bear insult and ridicule.

"And now, Dr. Finlay, if we may ask. . . ."

Before Reed could finish, Finlay was on his feet. Of course! The doctors could ask him anything they wished. He would tell them everything that he knew. They could have the notes on all his experiments. They could have copies of every speech that he had made in defense of the theory. He bustled out of the room. He was back again in several minutes, balancing in his little hands several notebooks and a half dozen or so thick folders. Perched precariously on top of the lot were a test tube and a small bowl half full of water. Reed noticed a tiny curl of black substance clinging to the inner side of the bowl, just under the lip.

Finlay deposited his cargo on a table beside Reed.

"It's all there," he cried. "All that you need. Take it all. Keep it as long as you like."

The little man was too excited to sit down; he strode up and down the room as the three visitors began their questions. Finlay walked with a bouncing gait, up on the balls of his feet; sometimes his hands were locked behind his back as he answered their questions; sometimes they were in front of him, making little circles and pointing.

He explained his basic reasons for abandoning the fomites theory 19 years before. They were the very same reasons that had caused Lazear—and now Reed—to lose confidence in the theory. Yellow jack too often failed to spread to people who had been in contact with the sick and their possessions. And too often the fever struck down just one person in a large group.

"One little, delicate mosquito. The female of the species."

Why, of all insects, had he chosen the mosquito? Simple. Yellow jack struck in the summer, the mosquito season. It limited itself to the warm climates of the world, the mosquito climates. It literally bounced from person to person, instead of spreading forth in a uniform manner, suggesting an insect that flies, the mosquito.

"But we understand," Reed asked, "that you have narrowed your suspicion down to one type of mosquito?"

"That's right. Absolutely right!" Finlay paused in his walking and, forefinger upraised, struck such a theatrical pose that Carroll almost laughed aloud. "One little, delicate, beautiful mosquito. The female of the species. *Culex fasciatus*."

"Why did you select that particular mosquito?"

Basically there were three reasons. First, most of the cases Finlay had seen were in the city, and the *Culex fasciatus* was a city mosquito. Second, he had sighted her often in the houses of the sick; she seemed to like to cling to the rafters in a room, away from the windows and out of the wind, though at times she was found in pools of stagnant water outside. Third, because she was basically a household insect, she was the one most likely to avoid death in the street cleanings that accompanied every fever epidemic; perhaps that was why those water-and-mop campaigns had never achieved any success against the disease.

Carroll, who was the only man in the room still genuinely skeptical of Finlay's idea, leaned toward Lazear and whispered. "He's guessing. Just guessing!"

Lazear shot him a hard look. "Maybe. And maybe he's the best blessed guesser you'll ever meet."

Finlay hurried on, paying no attention to the exchange, his shining eyes on Reed.

He quickly ran through a description of the female *Culex fasciatus*. She was a pretty thing, with stripes across the back and almost transparent wings. She fed on the blood of human beings only after she had mated; she refused to lay her eggs unless filled with that blood. She did not bite at night, and the male of the species did not bite at all. She liked

[81]

stagnant water, and would lay her eggs where any was available—in an old wash basin, pan, dish, rain barrel, even a flower bowl.

He stopped at the table alongside Reed and pointed down at the bowl he had placed there; suddenly Reed understood the little black smears clinging to the inside of its lip. Finlay saw the expression on Reed's face.

"Yes, Major. They are the eggs of the *Culex fasciatus.* If you look closely, you'll see that they're merely little black cylinders at the moment. But put them in a warm, wet place and they will hatch out in three days. Give them another week for the larva stage, and then another two for the pupa stage. Then the female will be ready to spread the infection of yellow fever."

He beckoned Lazear and Carroll to join him. They came forward—Lazear with eagerness, Carroll with the lukewarm interest of the skeptic trying to be polite—and stared down at the black smears.

"I want you to take these with you," Finlay said. "It will save you the difficulty and the very precious time of searching out your own specimens. I was keeping them for my own future experiments, but that is of no matter now. You must have them."

Lazear touched the rim of the bowl, almost reverently, Reed thought. "How long have you had these eggs, sir?"

Finlay thought for a moment. "I'm not quite sure. Over a month, surely."

"And they didn't dry up on you?"

"Oh, no. And it would not have mattered if they had. They're very hardy little things, these eggs. The mother lays them on the surface of the water. It does not matter if the water then dries up and leaves them stranded. They can lie where they are for months, in hot or freezing weather. They simply refuse to die. If you restore them to warmth and moisture . . ." Finlay snapped his fingers to emphasize his point, "they will hatch out immediately! Amazing, isn't it?"

One of the great problems facing the Army doctors, Finlay explained, would be to force the mosquitoes to feed on yellow fever victims. Oh, they were quite content, when flying free, to feed on any human being at hand. The prevalence of the fever in the Caribbean was ample proof of that. But when they were being held the prisoners of medical research—ah, that was a different matter. Their sole concern then was to fly away. That, of course, was exactly the thing that a researcher did not want them to do. Right? Finlay laughed as though he had made a great joke.

"And so," he said, "I've worked out a technique for preventing their escape." He gestured with the vial. "You are to keep them in test tubes, one to a tube. Each tube should be stoppered with a piece of cotton. Now, Major Reed, your arm, if I may—"

Obediently, Reed extended his arm. Finlay, as if lecturing children, spoke very precisely. "When the mosquito is ready to feed, place the test tube upside down an inch or so above the fever patient's arm or abdomen, thus. This will cause the mosquito to fly upwards, toward the bottom of the tube. Now carefully pick the cotton from the neck of the tube."

Carefully, as though the vial was actually stoppered and

as though it contained a precious mosquito, Finlay panto-mined the removal of the cotton. His eyes gleamed behind his spectacles. His great side whiskers quivered as his mouth worked with his concentration.

"Now, quickly lower the tube to the patient. Do nothing to further perturb the mosquito. You may have to wait quite a time. Slowly the mosquito will circle downward and downward until—poof!—she is at her meal!"

Reed had to smile to himself. Throughout the meeting, he had looked on Finlay as a comic and pathetic figure. Yet, the little man had so captured his attention these last moments that he now jumped slightly, as if the long beak of the female *Culex fasciatus* was actually boring into his arm. He heard Carroll snort. Reed glanced sheepishly at him.

"Let her have her fill," Finlay instructed softly and precisely. "Then, when she is finished, tap the tube." He clicked his fingernail against the glass. "She will fly upwards again. Lift the tube. Quickly stopper it."

He lifted his eyes to the doctors. They shone with the triumph of a man who has just completed a very delicate operation. "There! A simple little procedure, but an important one. It will save you a great many mosquitoes."

Carroll was staring down at his boot tips. There was a tightness in his hawklike face that Reed, from a long personal association with the man, recognized immediately. It was the tightness that got into Carroll's face when he was doing his almighty best to hold back his laughter.

Finlay suddenly became aware of Carroll's reaction to him. A slight flush crept into his face, and he aimed his next words—and icy words they were—directly at the physician.

"And, *Doctor*, be especially careful to use the very same procedure in the next step of your work—when you use its bite to induce a case of yellow fever in a laboratory animal or a man. Remember, it is filled with the venom of yellow fever. You don't want it escaping and flying off to spread its disease, do you?"

Carroll lifted his hawklike face to Finlay. There was still a tightness in it, but it was not the tightness of suppressed amusement.

"We'll soon see whether or not your mosquito spreads the fever."

All Carroll's skepticism of the theory was evident in his quiet, level tone.

The three doctors thanked Finlay and prepared to take their leave. Carroll took the notebooks and folders. Lazear quickly made for the bowl containing the *Culex fasciatus* eggs; it seemed as if he could not wait to get his hands on them. Reed smiled. For the first time in weeks, joy and youth were back in Jesse's face.

Finlay talked enthusiastically as he escorted his guests from the house, repeating all his instructions for the handling of the mosquitoes. At the gate, he wrung Reed's hand and Lazear's and even Carroll's.

"You're doing a wonderful thing," he said. "A wonderful thing. For all of mankind. I can't thank you enough. To see a glimmer of trust after all these years."

The officers climbed into a wagon for the ride to camp. Finlay waved and called out again and again his wishes for good luck as the wagon moved off down the dusty road.

When Finlay could no longer be seen or heard, Carroll

leaned forward and struck his knee, releasing all the laughter that he had held locked within himself for so long. He laughed until tears ran down his cheeks.

"Did you see him? Did you see him pottering about with that test tube? You would have thought he had figured out the most delicate, the most difficult, experiment in the world!"

"Don't make fun of him, Jim," Lazear said. "He couldn't help himself. He was just very happy."

Carroll gulped to stifle another burst of laughter. "I know, and I'm sorry. I don't mean to ridicule him. But he was comical. You've got to admit that, Jesse, You do, you know."

"I don't care. He's got the answer to this yellow fever business. That's all that matters to me."

"You really believe that, Jesse? You really think that he's not just an old fool making wild guesses?"

"I do."

Carroll stared for a brief moment at Lazear clutching the little bowl, protecting it against the lurch and bump of the wagon. Lazear had his knees pressed together. He looked like a child guarding a new and delicate toy. Again Carroll went off into gales of laughter. Even the always serious Lazear had to smile.

Reed sat toward the rear of the wagon. He stared at the dirt road leading back to Finlay's house. He was not even aware of Carroll's laughter. He was thinking that very soon he would have to experiment with a human life.

Chapter 7

August Battle

The Yellow Fever Commission began its study of Dr. Carlos Finlay's mosquito theory on August 1, 1900.

Reed had decided that his doctors should work along two fronts simultaneously. Not only would they investigate Finlay's idea as to how yellow fever was spread, but they would continue their search for the germ responsible for the disease, though past experience indicated that they had little hope of ever finding it.

Lazear was placed in charge of the Finlay study. He deserved the honor for two reasons: he was the only one of the four Commissioners to have pressed for the study; and, because of his work with malaria, he was the only one with any practical experience in the handling of mosquitoes.

The responsibility for finding the yellow fever germ was handed to Agramonte and Carroll. Agramonte, just back from Pinar del Rio now that the danger there had passed, was to carry on with his autopsies at Hospital Number One, and Carroll was to continue his microscopic studies of the blood and tissue samples brought to the Camp Columbia laboratory. Both men were also to take instructions from Lazear in the techniques of raising and feeding mosquitoes.

The change in Jesse Lazear relieved and pleased Reed. Jesse no longer cursed his microscope or stalked morosely through the wards at Havana and Camp Columbia. He was certain that the Commission was finally on the right track, and that they would very soon know how yellow jack worked its way from person to person. Then they could devise a method for wiping it out. After that the Commission could search for the germ responsible for the disease.

Lazear built a warm, moist nest for the mosquito eggs that Finlay had provided. He sent a sample of the eggs to the Department of Agriculture in Washington, asking for confirmation of Finlay's identification of the mosquitoes. Dr. L. O. Howard, head of the Department's Bureau of Entomology, confirmed Finlay's mosquitoes as *Culex fasciatus.*

In the time that Finlay had predicted, the eggs passed through the larval and pupal stages, evolving into full grown mosquitoes ready to suck the venom from yellow fever patients. Lazear placed the females in test tubes, giving each mosquito a number. He stoppered the tubes with cotton, inserted each in a cloth bag as a precaution against breakage, and arranged them in a small rack that could be easily carried around the fever wards.

But, before he had the chance to venture forth on his first feeding expedition, two things happened that had a direct bearing on the work of the Commission.

First, for no apparent reason, the epidemic at Quemados went into an abrupt decline, giving every indication that it would soon die out. This meant that there would be fewer fever patients from whom the mosquitoes could suck the all important venom of the fever. Lazear, accordingly, turned his attention to Havana. Hospital Number One and its neighbor, Las Animas Hospital, still had more fever patients than they could handle.

Second, at the end of the first week in August, Reed was summoned back to the United States. The recommendations that he had made the year before with Drs. Shakespeare and Vaughan on the control of typhoid fever in Army camps in the United States had yet to be written into a final report. Surgeon General Sternberg wanted him to complete that report as soon as possible. Dr. Shakespeare had died early in the summer, and Reed was to work with Dr. Vaughan in Washington.

Reed looked on the return home with mixed emotions. On the one hand, he hated the very thought of leaving Cuba just now. He and his Commission had come through a living torture to reach the present point in their studies. Deep rooted in him now was a faith in Finlay's theory. He was sure that it was going to lead the Commission to the solution of the yellow fever problem. He wanted to be there when that happened.

But, on the other hand, he could not help but feel a rising tide of elation at the thought of returning to his family. Once again he would see and hold his beloved Emilie. Once again he would see young Walter, grown now so much taller than his father. He had missed his family very much during these long weeks in Cuba.

Reed boarded a small steamer the day after he received his orders. Lazear, Carroll, Agramonte, and several other doctors from Camp Columbia went down to the dock to see him off. They told him to hurry back; they told him that they were going to miss his leadership. What were they going to do,

Major Reed felt a premonition as he waved goodbye.

Lazear asked, when their tempers flared and he wasn't around to calm them down? Reed stood at the ship's rail, waving to them as the anchor came rattling up out of the filthy harbor water. He felt the deck begin to tremble underfoot, and his three friends began to slide away from view.

He kept on waving until he could no longer see them, until they had become so small that they had faded into the background of dock buildings. The ship passed beneath the shadow of Morro Castle, situated at the mouth of the harbor. He felt the bow rise to the first swell of deep water. The buildings of Havana slowly turned into a long blur of white. He saw the full greenness of the island, rising behind the city and touching the cloudless sky.

He stared down at the foam rolling from under the ship back toward that island of so much beauty and so much death. Suddenly he was cold all over, shivering, filled with the senseless urge to hurry back to the island. He gripped the rail so hard that his knuckles turned white. It was the only way that he could restrain himself from dashing to the bridge and ordering the captain to put him overside in a launch. The reasonable part of his mind tried to tell him that the fear within him was silly. He had a premonition that something terrible was going to happen while he was gone.

Jesse Lazear never once varied his morning routine in the next weeks. In the morning he stopped at Agramonte's laboratory and put into his metal tray the test tubes containing the mosquitoes scheduled for feeding that day; then he went to Las Animas Hospital and Hospital Number One. He sought in each ward the most seriously ill. At each bed, he set down his metal tray, and he cheerfully explained the purpose of his visit. He told each newcomer that what he wanted to do was painless and might be of help in knocking out the yellow jack. If the patient knew about his visits, Lazear grinned and remarked that his "birds" needed breakfast. The patient would grin back weakly and murmur something such as, "Fire away, Doc." It was difficult, even through all the pain and nausea, not to like this bearded doctor with his easy going way.

With humorous gravity, Lazear would bow, roll back the patient's sleeve, select a tube from the tray, turn it upside down, quickly remove the cotton stopper, and press the mouth of the tube against the patient's arm. Muttering to the mosquito, he would coax her downward until she settled on the patient and began her meal. When she was done, he would tap the glass lightly, causing her to fly upward. Then he would stopper the tube, write for a moment in his notebook, thank the patient, and move on to the next bed.

When his rounds were done, he carried his little tray back to Agramonte's laboratory. His next task was to double-check the feedings for that day in his notebook. Then, after storing his mosquitoes away in their warm, moist shelter, he returned to Camp Columbia. By this time it was evening.

Lazear's work during those weeks in August was no secret. He could not have kept it a secret, even if he had wanted to. Word of what he was doing quickly went from patient to patient, spreading far beyond the fever wards. It reached the doctors and the nurses and the orderlies. Did you hear? Dr. Lazear's got it into his head that mosquitoes carry the yellow jack. Old Finlay's idea. Lazear's walking about, big as life, feeding mosquitoes on the patients. Too bad Reed isn't here. He'd put a stop to the whole thing. What? Reed's in favor of it? But that can't be! He's too sensible. The word got outside the hospital grounds and into Havana.

The doctors of the area soon came to see for themselves

what was going on. It was to be expected; they had never been able to ignore Finlay and his fussy but meteoric mind. The doctors were divided in their reaction to the current work of the Commission. Some had long made sport of Finlay and were quite ready to turn their ridicule on anyone who dared follow in his footsteps. Lazear pleased them mightily. He was the perfect target, with that thrusting walk of his and that intense look in his eyes. Not a few had always been suspicious of him, as the normal always are suspicious of genius. Now, they told themselves, we know for sure: he's quite off his head. Just another Finlay, trotting about with his little tray full of test tubes and mosquitoes. They smugly awaited his failure—for fail he surely must!

Others, however, had heard of Finlay's theory through the years and had wondered from time to time if perhaps the old man might not have something after all, even though his attempts to pass the yellow fever from his mosquitoes to laboratory animals had failed miserably. These men had looked at the fomites theory and had found it wanting; they had supported it only because it was the proper medical thing to do. Now they came to watch Lazear, and, though they sometimes smiled for the benefit of their doubting colleagues, they hoped in their heart of hearts that he could find something that Finlay had overlooked, something—anything—that would help rid the land of the curse known as yellow jack.

By the second week the entire medical population at Havana, military and civilian alike, was watching Lazear with deep interest. Then Lazear put Finlay's theory to its ultimate tests. He began to search for men who would be willing to have his mosquitoes bite them. He deliberately closed his mind to the fact that he was endangering human life. The experiment had to be performed. There was no other way to prove or disprove Finlay's theory.

The skeptics, of course, now thought that he had gone completely insane. He's playing God, they said. We know the experiment will never work, but nevertheless, how dare he ask men to flirt with death? And who will be fool enough to listen to him?

Within the week, Lazear found nine men who agreed to the experiment; one or two even looked him up and volunteered. They were young men, most of them Americans from the surrounding garrisons and the wards of Hospital One. Two were Cubans in the employ of the Army; they agreed to the test as a sort of lark. They had heard the doctors in town speak about the mosquitoes; everyone knew there was nothing to fear from the little beasts.

When a man consented to become a human guinea pig, Lazear hurried him to Agramonte's laboratory, sat him down, and explained again the danger involved. He spoke of the good that the test might accomplish. He assured the man that, should he catch yellow fever, he would be given the best medical care. He told the man to leave if he no longer had heart for the job. Lazear ended by saying that the whole affair might fail. Each man seemed to think that this would be the case. When all was said that had to be said, Lazear told the man to roll up his sleeve.

Among those nine men who bared their arms to Lazear, there were several ward orderlies who wanted to do something for medical science. Two infantrymen volunteered simply because they liked Lazear and felt sorry for him. One soldier could not explain his presence. He just felt that he was doing the right thing. Yellow jack had killed his buddy earlier in the summer. He guessed that was why he was there.

Lazear lost much sleep during that second week in August. He was calm in front of the men, smiling and conversing with them, even kidding when they showed a glimmer of fear at the sight of the mosquitoes. But, in the silent hours of the night, he tossed and turned with worry. He saw yellowed faces coming at him from out of the dark, and he wondered how he would ever be able to live with himself if one of those men died.

But he worried in vain. Not one of the men fell ill in the next week and a half. Lazear checked them daily. Their temperatures did not rise. They had no pains in their legs, arms, or backs. Their faces and eyes remained clear. Helplessly, Lazear watched them pass safely out of the time period required for the incubation of yellow fever. The test was a complete failure.

He had been worried about making men sick; now he was more upset that they had remained healthy. He stumbled blindly into Agramonte's laboratory and put his face into his hands. Was it possible that he had put all his faith in a thing of no value? Was it possible that Finlay was wrong? Was it possible that, after all, the female *Culex fasciatus* was just a harmless little beast?

He knew that he was the laughing stock of a great part of the Havana medical world. Many doctors had been waiting to see him fall flat on his face. Well, he had certainly obliged. He saw the look of sympathy in Agramonte's eyes. He heard Carroll, who had always been so skeptical of the whole theory, quietly ask if he intended trying the experiment again. He appreciated the man's decency for not saying "I told you so."

And he saw Finlay. The old man was in the laboratory every day, peering at the mosquitoes, bouncing about, insisting that some error must have caused the experiment to fail. It wasn't the fault of his precious mosquitoes. They carried the yellow jack, all right. The failure was Lazear's fault. Lazear pressed his lips into a thin line and held his temper. He deafened his ears to Finlay's prattle. He turned away from Agramonte's sympathetic eyes. He answered Carroll's question with a defiant, "Of course I'm going to try the test again. When, in science, did one failure ever kill an experiment?"

Carroll grinned, and Lazear thought he saw admiration in that hawklike face. "If at first you don't succeed, try, try again, eh?"

"That's about it," Lazear said. "It could be that Finlay is right—that the failure is with me and not the mosquitoes."

"Perhaps, Jesse. Perhaps. However, I doubt it very much." He put his hand on Lazear's shoulder. "But carry on, and good luck. Let me know if you need any help."

"Thanks, Jim. But I think everything is going to be all right."

Lazear hoped that he sounded more confident than he felt. The more he thought about the theory, the more he wondered if he was wasting his time. He wondered if his desire to go on with it was grounded in the disheartening fact that he had nowhere else to turn.

He stubbornly forced himself back to his daily routine. He fed his mosquitoes on the arms and stomachs of new fever patients carefully, writing down each step. When the first batch of his "birds" began to die, he tended their eggs and brought into being a second generation. He grinned when the patients asked, "You gonna spend your whole life with them varmints, Doc?" The ward jokes about the theory hurt, but he didn't show it. He behaved as if his faith was as bright and shining to him as ever.

Though outwardly he appeared calm and confident, his mind was torn with questions, even when he slept. Why did the test fail? Were the mosquitoes really the villains? Was there something in the whole affair that he had failed to see? Had he made any mistakes along the way?

The answer to that last question was "No!" He had fed the mosquitoes on the deadliest fever cases he could find before turning them loose on the nine men. They had all been mature cases, all of them four, five, and six days old. No, no, he was sure that he had made no mistakes. Driven to distraction by these questions, he did something that the Commission had decided against. He turned a mosquito loose on himself. The Commission had had a very practical reason for deciding against experimentation on its own members. They were not afraid of the disease, but they knew that their study would be slowed or halted altogether if they landed flat on their backs with the yellow jack.

Experimenting upon himself was a desperation move. Perhaps he could succeed where nine others had failed. And he no longer had the heart to put up with the scornful looks he got when he went looking for new human guinea pigs.

But he remained perfectly well. The *Culex fasciatus* had missed again. Ten tries. Ten failures. That should be enough for anyone. He felt the last shred of his faith turn to dust.

On August 27 he went to Agramonte's laboratory and told the doctor what he had done. Agramonte had only to look at him to know the result. Lazear shook his head disgustedly. He was ready to call it quits. Finlay's theory had once looked so beautiful and so neat, but now he guessed that it deserved all the skepticism it had received in the past 19 years. Lazear felt like a fool.

Agramonte listened sympathetically and asked, "If you're ready to quit, then why have you brought your tray of test tubes with you?"

Lazear shrugged. "Habit, I guess. I thought I'd plug along with them until Reed returns. Then we can sit down and decide what to do next."

Agramonte nodded slowly. "I see."

He grinned to himself after Lazear had left the laboratory. So Lazear was ready to throw in the sponge, was he? Agramonte doubted that. He had heard too many stubborn men say that they were going to quit when actually they were just beginning to fight.

Lazear got back to his laboratory at Camp Columbia at one o'clock in the afternoon. He climbed down from the wagon and reflected that his morning had been positively miserable. After he had left Agramonte, he had gone mechanically about his feeding rounds in the wards. Perhaps it was the state of his nerves, but the patients had seemed downright uncooperative. In their eyes he had seen their unspoken words, "Look, Doc, we feel terrible. Maybe we're even dying. Can't you leave us in peace for even one day?" Then one of the mosquitoes had given him trouble.

He stopped at the foot of the steps rising to the laboratory. He thought about that mosquito and, as he had done all during the ride from Havana, tried to figure out what was ailing her. He had tried to make her feed on four patients this morning. She had refused everytime. This made two days in a row that she had gone without a meal. She was on the point of dying of starvation.

He went back over her feeding record; like those of all his "birds," he had committed it to memory. He recalled that she had bitten her first patient 12 days ago, August 15, and that the patient had been in the second day of the fever. She had been fed again on the 21st, 23rd, and 25th. Since the 25th, she had been starving herself. If she didn't feed soon, she would die.

He went up the steps and into the laboratory. Carroll was sitting there, bending over a microscope. He looked up and said he was studying a blood sample from a victim just dead of yellow fever at Las Animas Hospital.

"Any luck?" Lazear asked listlessly.

"Negative. How about you?"

"What do you think?" Lazear walked, shoulders forward, to a nearby work table and slammed the tray down upon it. "The fact is, things are so bad that I can't even get one of the mosquitoes to feed on a patient. Even she must sense the entire operation is a waste of time. She's refused a meal for two days now."

Carroll rose from his microscope and crossed to Lazear.

"That's strange, isn't it?"

"I guess so," Lazear said. "It doesn't matter. She'll be dead by morning."

"Let's have a look at her."

Lazear glanced sharply at Carroll. "You really want to see her?"

"Of course. I wouldn't have asked if I didn't."

Lazear shrugged his surprise. He removed the tube from the rack and took it out of its little cloth bag. He handed the tube to Carroll, who carried it to a window and held it up to the sunlight. The mosquito clung listlessly to the glass. Carroll pursed his lips and came back to the table.

"She does look a bit on the tired side."

"That's an understatement."

"She's going to starve to death, eh?"

"If she doesn't feed soon."

Carroll returned the test tube to Lazear.

"Well, let's see what we can do about that."

Astonished, Lazear saw him begin to roll up his sleeve. "You're going to let her feed on you?"

"That's the idea."

"Don't be silly."

"What's so silly about giving poor little Doris someting to eat. It's all in the cause of humanity," Carroll said with mock seriousness.

"You know what we agreed. We're not to experiment on ourselves just yet."

Carroll's eyes swung round to Lazear. "You've taken the bite, haven't you?"

"How did you know that?" Lazear asked sharply.

"Agramonte talked with me on the phone about an hour ago. So now it's my turn."

"But this thing might be loaded with yellow jack."

"Then I'll fall sick and perhaps die."

"It's a possibility."

"One that we both doubt very much. Agramonte says you've lost your faith in Finlay's theory. And about time, too, I should think," Carroll said. "Believe me, if I felt there was any danger to this, I wouldn't try it. After all, old friend, I've got a wife and five kiddies back in the States. Come on, let the lady have her feed."

By this time, Lazear was amused. He would never figure out Carroll. One minute Carroll told you the mosquitoes were useless; the next minute, he was ready to let one feed on him.

Automatically, because by now it was second nature Lazear went through the routine that Finlay had taught him.

He pressed the mouth of the tube against Carroll's exposed arm. The mosquito, suddenly turned upside down, did not even bother to fly up to the base of the tube. She clung to the glass wall and fluttered her wings once or twice. She moved her silver beak almost imperceptibly. Lazear made a disgusted noise. He clicked the glass with his fingernail, muttering to her to go down where she belonged.

"Does she understand English?" Carroll asked innocently.

Lazear clicked the glass again. No response. He started to remove the tube, but Carroll stopped him, taking the vial and holding it in place. Carroll strolled over to a high stool and sat down. Lazear followed him. They stared for several minutes at the tube with its mouth against Carroll's arm.

Suddenly the mosquito began to drift downward in a series of lazy circles. She settled on Carroll's arm and remained motionless for so long that Lazear muttered:

"Oh, come on! Get it over with."

Carroll laughed. "I think she's heard you."

And it seemed that she had, for the mosquito drew her legs up against her sides—her biting stance—and pressed her silver beak against Carroll's arm. Slowly, almost reluctantly, she drove her beak beneath the skin.

"That's more like it," Carroll commented. "Drink away, old girl. Can't have you dying on my friend Jesse."

Lazear looked at Carroll from beneath level brows. He said, "Thanks, Jim."

"Think nothing of it."

The mosquito drank her fill. A large welt appeared on Carroll's arm.

Chapter 8

The Saga of James Carroll

O n August 29th, Carroll walked into Las Animas Hospital to pick up several blood samples and to accompany Lazear on the rounds of the fever wards. Agramonte noticed he was pale, drawn, and without energy. Carroll's skeptical wit was missing. Though the jokes of the patients gave him ample opportunity, he did not bother to chide Lazear about the Finlay experiment. Agramonte decided that the weather and the job were getting the man down.

Only once did Carroll show any real interest in the work at hand. At the third bed visited, he moved a step forward and asked Lazear:

"That's 'Bird 12,' isn't it?"

Lazear didn't take his eyes off the test tube. "Yes."

"How's she doing?"

"Fine. She's quite lively today."

Carroll cast Agramonte an amused glance. "Lazear can

thank me that this little beast is alive. She was almost dead the other day, but I gave her a meal."

"Wasn't that rather dangerous?"

"Of course not. We all know there's nothing to this mosquito business."

Agramonte looked closely at Carroll. He saw him touch his fingertips to his forehead. The man was deathly pale. There were dark splashes under his eyes that had not been in his face earlier in the week.

Agramonte left Las Animas with Lazear and Carroll about an hour later. They rode along the road towards Quemados. Carroll shifted uncomfortably in the wagon as it jounced along the road, his face showing pain now and again. Agramonte got down from the wagon near Hospital Number One. Before he walked away, he looked up at Carroll.

"I'd get a good night's sleep if I were you," he said. "You look a little washed out."

Carroll nodded. "I can't say I feel particularly well. I'll take your advice. I never was one to sit up all night staring into a microscope."

Agramonte watched the wagon move off. He walked slowly, thoughtfully, towards Hospital Number One.

Carroll went down for an afternoon swim the next day. He came slowly out of the water and toweled himself dry. He was disappointed. He had hoped that a few minutes in the ocean surf would make him feel better, lift his spirits a little. He stared up at the sky. The sun was overhead, blinding bright and hot. But Carroll saw that his arms and body were covered with goose pimples. A little chill ran through him. Perhaps he was coming down with the grippe. Perhaps he had been working too hard.

He finished toweling himself and walked slowly back to the hospital. The chill came and went again. He put his hand to his forehead. He wouldn't be surprised if he were feverish. His legs felt heavy. They ached a little.

Fine thing, he thought. Just the right time to get sick! A new batch of blood and sample tissues awaited him in the laboratory. Well, they would have to wait until morning. He was going to go to bed. He did not feel at all well.

The telephone in Agramonte's laboratory rang at dusk. "Aristides?" The urgent voice at the other end was Lazear's. "Yes?"

"Carroll's under the weather." Agramonte's fingers tightened about the receiver. "He went swimming this afternoon and came back with a chill. He thought he was coming down with the grippe. Now he's aching all over, and he's nauseated. He thinks he has a touch of malaria."

Agramonte asked slowly. "And what do you think it is?"

"I—don't know."

"Is he in bed now?"

"Yes. But he refuses to take the whole thing seriously. He says he'll be up and about in the morning."

"We'd better let him have an undisturbed night. I'll come out in the morning and check his blood. Perhaps it is malaria. If we find malaria parasites, then we'll know."

"All right."

"And, Jesse?"

"Yes?"

"Take it easy."

Lazear was up and dressed at dawn. He couldn't sleep. He could only toss and turn and wonder about Carroll.

He walked swiftly but quietly along the corridor of the officers's quarters, past the room that Reed had occupied and that was awaiting his return. He tapped Carroll's door lightly. Hearing no response, he pushed it open. Carroll was not in the room. His bed was unmade, the covers tumbled. Lazear walked swiftly across the still silent grounds to the laboratory. As he had expected, Carroll was in the laboratory, bent over a microscope. At the sound of the door opening and closing, Carroll spoke without looking up.

"Couldn't sleep, old lad? Worried about your chum?" The words were supposed to be light and gay, but his voice was tired and frightened. He was working by the light of a kerosene lantern. He did not raise his head as Lazear stepped forward. Lazear stared down at him and watched him adjust the lens of the microscope. Lazear knew what he was doing without asking.

Concentrating on the eyepiece, Carroll said, carelessly, "I've been checking a sample of my blood, looking for the malaria parasites. If I've got malaria, then I should see them quite clearly at this moment..." He gave his full attention to the microscope. "But..." He started to speak again, lifting his face at the same time. "I guess it's not malaria. Not a sign of the little beggars." He stared at Lazear.

Lazear caught the edge of the table and held it tightly. His legs seemed to turn to water. Carroll looked as if he had aged a hundred years overnight. His cheeks had caved in and had gone bloodless. His eyes were puffy and red-rimmed.

His hands trembled. He tried to smile.

"Pains in the arms and legs and back. Nausea. A mounting temperature," Carroll said softly. "I guess we both know what I've got."

"It can't have been the mosquito!"

As if he were some sort of caged animal, Lazear strode back and forth along the length of his laboratory. His shoulders were hunched forward, and his eyes were dulled with remorse. James Carroll had been in the fever ward for a day and a night now.

"There's every reason to believe the mosquito did not give him the fever. Ten men—myself included—were bitten this month. Not one of us fell ill. Now, why should Carroll take the fever from a bite when the rest of us did not? Are we all immune?"

Agramonte did not reply. He and Lazear had been over this very same ground a hundred times in the past 24 hours.

"But we're not all immune. At least I know that I'm not," Lazear went on, slapping the table to drive home his point.

He pushed on, "I've gone over practically every day of my life. I've tried to recall every childhood illness that ever bothered me. I can't recall one that even resembled the fever. No. No, it's not the mosquito. If it were, I would have fallen ill.

Lazear was pacing again, striking his hands together. "So the fever had to come from some other source. Carroll could have picked it up anywhere. He exposed himself to it constantly in the past weeks—everytime he walked through the wards, everytime he worked with the blood and tissue samples. He's . . ."

His voice trailed away. His shoulders sagged. He looked back at Agramonte. His voice was listless. "It's no use, is it? The arguments are no good. They just won't hold water."

Agramonte shrugged slowly, helplessly. All through the night, Lazear had followed a pattern. First, he would argue against the mosquito. Then, with lightning swiftness, he would argue in its favor. And then he would begin to blame himself for having allowed Carroll to take the bite.

Lazear came to the work table. He sat down heavily on the high stool. "We both know it was the mosquito."

"We have no proof, my friend," Agramonte said.

"But we sense it. Sense it so deeply that it's got to be the truth. It's too much of a coincidence that Carroll should take the fever from another source immediately after he had been bitten."

"It does seem strange," Agramonte admitted.

"It is the mosquito," Lazear said, his voice rising to a shout. "It is! And I allowed the thing to bite him. It's my fault that he's over in the fever ward!"

Agramonte said, more sharply than he had intended, "I've told you that you mustn't think that sort of thing."

"What else can I think? I'm to blame, and that's all there is to it. I could have stopped him."

"But you tried to warn him that the bite was possibly dangerous. He's admitted that himself."

"Oh, I tried, all right," Lazear said, staring down at the fists held tight against the table. "But I didn't try very hard. I didn't think that there was any real danger. I had lost all faith in the mosquito theory. I would not have allowed him to take the bite if I hadn't taken one myself and if it had not come to nothing."

"I know that, my friend. You've been going on for hours now, blaming yourself. And for no genuine reason. How many times must I remind you of one little fact that exonerates you of all blame. At one time during the feeding, you tried to remove the test tube from Carroll's arm. He stopped you and held it there himself."

Lazear's eyes blinked wide open. A heavy silence fell between the two men. Then Lazear said quietly, "Thank you, Aristides. That's just what I needed."

Agramonte leaned forward and spoke in a business-like fashion. "Listen, Jesse. We must not let worry about Carroll stop us from doing our work. We suspect that your mosquito gave Carroll the fever. That means that we've got to begin checking Finlay's theory all over again. There's just a possibility that it might be correct after all."

Carroll tossed on his narrow cot in the isolation ward. He was alternately chilling and burning with the fever. He felt as if he had been beaten for hours with a club. Every muscle and joint in his body ached. The breath came out of him in sharp gasps. With his head pushed hard against the pillow, he was grinning. A soft, rattling noise sounded deep in his throat. It was laughter. The laughter hurt his chest.

The lucid part of his mind told him that he must be pretty close to going out of his head and that he had better cut out the laughter. But he could not stop. The whole situation was just too funny. He had been the Commission's last hold-out against the mosquito theory, and yet here he was, flat on his back, proving the correctness of that theory.

He had chided Lazear and Finlay for their trust in the miserable little *Culex fasciatus*. He had even had his faith in Reed shaken when the Major had swung away from the fomites theory. And so what had he done? Of his own accord, he had rolled up his sleeve and had proved that their silly, impossible belief was, after all was said and done, the truth.

And it *was* the truth. In his own mind, he was dead certain of that. Oh, the scientists and the doctors wouldn't agree with him. They would say that his case proved nothing, that he might have picked up the fever in any number of places these past few days. They would shake their heads and say that they could not believe until they saw a case of yellow jack that could be traced back to nothing but the mosquito.

Well, let them think as they pleased. This good old case of the yellow fever came from the mosquito, and let's have no argument about it. He should know. He was the one who was flat on his back with it, wasn't he?

Now, he thought, if Lazear would just get back to work. He had a possible proof for his theory. It was up to him to take it from there. It was up to him to turn his little "birds" loose on a few more arms and produce cases of fever to remove all doubt.

Carroll stopped laughing. He turned his head painfully on the pillow. He was worried about Lazear. He wondered if

Jesse had lost his courage. He was blaming himself for what had happened. He had hovered over Carroll's bed like an old woman. Carroll couldn't really blame Lazear for his feelings. Lazear thought he was going to die.

Carroll grinned through his pain. He'd fool Lazear. He'd fool them all. He wasn't going to kick off. Not just yet. What would that fine little lady of his and their five youngsters up there in the states do if he decided to bow out now? He felt a great tiredness wash over him. The world started to slip away from him. He fought to keep his hold on consciousness.

Darkness closed round him. He slept, his face jerking now and again with the pain in him.

Reed stared down at the letter in his hand. He shook his head, as if someone had just hit him very hard. He was deathly pale. Jim Carroll had the yellow fever. It couldn't be. Not Carroll.

But it was true. The proof of it was right before his eyes, the proof written in Jesse Lazear's strong handwriting. Carroll was now in the hospital, fighting for his life. His gums had begun to bleed the very day the letter had been written. The yellowness was in his face. He was very weak and his temperature was running high, well over 103 degrees.

Reed's legs felt weak under him. Jim Carroll was 47 years old. He had always looked on himself as a hardy, tough man. But that was his own opinion of himself. In Reed's estimation, Carroll was aging. The fever had a way of being especially hard on aging men.

Reed walked to his desk. He sat down. He told himself he must act calmly now. He had a terrible job to perform.

He took up a pen and began to write:

"My dear Mrs. Carroll:

I'm afraid that I have bad news . . . "

Agramonte said, "It's about time that you had a change of heart."

Lazear sat down at the work table. His face was flushed from the sun, and he was perspiring. He had just returned to the laboratory from a visit with Carroll. There was an expression of wonder in his eyes.

"You can thank our bald-headed friend for my change of heart as you call it," he said. "He could hardly talk, but he told me that he'd break my neck if I didn't get on with the work. I couldn't turn him down. No matter how I felt."

Agramonte grinned. "Good for him."

The expression of wonder in Lazear's eyes deepened. "He's quite a man. He believes in the theory. It doesn't matter to him that he might have picked up the fever in a dozen places. He *believes* in the mosquito. Of all people, he's the one who's come to have some faith in it."

Lazear shook his head in disbelief. Then he pulled himself to his feet. "Well, let's get started. I don't want to have my neck broken."

Agramonte asked, "Have you anyone in mind for the experiment?"

Lazear shook his head. He went to the shelf where the test tubes containing his mosquitoes were kept. "Not yet," he said.

In turn, he held the tubes up to the light. He nodded with satisfaction. His little "birds" were all alive and healthy.

He noticed that one of the tubes was cracked. He felt a chill run through him. The occupant was mosquito number 12. He had the sudden urge to smash the tube and snuff out the life of this tiny insect that had sent Carroll to the isolation ward. Then he shrugged and knew that he would merely transfer the bird to new living quarters. The insect was a senseless thing. It was not her fault that she harbored murder. He walked toward the veranda. He would make the switch-over to a new tube out there. The light was better. Then he remembered that he had intended to add something to his reply to Agramonte's question.

He said, "I plan to ask the first person I meet."

At 11 o'clock in the morning, Private William Dean of the Seventh Cavalry, with an hour of free time on his hands, was taking a stroll. He paused at the foot of the steps rising to the frame building, his big face wrinkled with curiosity. There at the top, his brows knitted in concentration, was Dr. Jesse Lazear. Dean knew he should walk on; a good soldier does not stand around and stare at an officer at work. But he could not drag himself away. Lazear was holding two test tubes. He had their open mouths pressed together, and he seemed to be trying to coax whatever was in one test tube into the other. Dean was a little too far away for a really good view.

He spoke before he could stop himself.

"Morning, Doctor."

He threw Lazear one of this best salutes as the doctor glanced in his direction. The appearance of Lazear's face shocked him. If being a doctor and an officer caused you to look as bad as Lazear looked at this moment, then Private Dean was very happy to be playing second fiddle to a lot of horses with the Seventh Cavalry.

Lazear returned the soldier's greeting. He did not re-

"You *still* fooling with your mosquitoes, Doc?"

turn the salute, however, for both hands were occupied with the test tubes.

Dean heard the doctor's greeting with a practiced ear. There had been no annoyance in the tone. You had to listen carefully to how officers spoke to determine what to do next with them. No animosity in Lazear's answer meant that Private Dean might move a little closer for a better look at the test tubes. He came slowly up the steps.

Now he could make out the mosquito. It stubbornly refused to move itself from one tube to another. Dean listened to Lazear talking to it as though it could understand him, coaxing it along. Then he asked, "You still fooling with your mosquitoes, Doc?"

Lazear did not raise his eyes. "Looks that way, doesn't it?"

"Do you really think they cause the yellow jack, like everybody says you believe?"

"Not cause," Lazear said. "Spread."

Suddenly, as if it had enough of annoying Lazear, the mosquito worked her way over into the empty tube. Lazear quickly stoppered the tube. He looked up, saw Dean, and blinked. Dean had the impression Lazear was really seeing him for the first time that morning.

"What's your name, soldier?"

"Private William H. Dean, sir. Seventh Cavalry."

"I see." Lazear gave him another long look. "Interested in mosquitoes?"

Dean thought the question over for a minute. He scratched his head. "Can't rightly say I ever thought much about them one way or the other, sir."

"How long have you been in Cuba?"

"Close on a year, sir."

"Go into Havana often?"

"No, sir. I don't care for it very much. Fact of the matter, I haven't been out of camp for two months now."

"Ever been over to the isolation wards?"

"You mean where the fever is, sir?"

"Yes."

"Oh, no, sir."

"Then you've not been exposed to yellow jack in the past month?"

"Not if I could help it, sir."

"Have you ever had the fever?"

"No, sir."

Lazear held the test tube up to the sunlight coming through a crack in the wooden awning above the laboratory-doorway. He released a sigh, as if he had reached some sort of decision.

"What do you think of my 'bird,' Dean?"

"Kind of pretty, sir," Dean said.

"Would you let her bite you?"

Dean's mouth fell open. He snapped it shut.

"You kidding, Doc?"

"No. I've never been more serious in my life."

"What're you trying to do, Doc? See if you can give me the yellow jack?"

"That's exactly what I'm trying to do."

Then Dean listened while the doctor talked about the mosquito. It all fitted in with what Dean had heard a couple of days ago. Doctor Carroll, the bald headed one was over in the fever ward, flat on his back. Lazear said that this very mosquito was possibly the cause for Carroll being over there. Carroll had taken a bite from it several days ago. Lazear thought that the mosquito had given him the yellow jack.

"But I can't be sure. A doctor can never be sure from the

results of just one experiment. I've got to try it again. And then again. If it works enough times, then I'll know that I may have the answer to how yellow fever is spread." Lazear paused, regarded him steadily. "Well, what about it, Dean? I need your help. Will you take a bite?"

A little wave of fear started up in Dean. But he grinned as if he didn't know what fear was.

"Sure, Doc, I ain't afraid of that little thing."

Lazear nodded tersely. He said, "Thank you, Dean."

Dean now became aware of a third man on the porch. He was that darkskinned doctor who worked with Lazear. His face was calm, but Dean knew that he had come running as soon as Lazear had asked about letting the "bird" do some biting. Lazear conferred with the Cuban doctor, then looked at Dean and said, "Come on in, soldier."

Private Dean walked into the cool interior of the laboratory. He rolled up his sleeve and took his place in medical history.

Chapter 9

The Greater Saga of Jesse Lazear

Reed brushed past the lieutenant who held the door open for him at Surgeon General George Sternberg's Washington, D.C. office. In Reed's hand was a telegram which he waved excitedly at the gray-haired general. Sternberg smiled, half rising.

"More news from Lazear?"

"Yes, sir."

"And, from the look on your face, I can tell that it's good news."

"Indeed it is!"

The door closed as the lieutenant, Sternberg's secretary, returned to his desk in the outer office. Sternberg gestured Reed to the chair alongside his massive cluttered desk. Sternberg dropped into his own seat, a leather upholstered swivel chair, and leaned far back in it. He clasped his hands across his stomach.

"Well, let's hear it."

Reed leaned forward, grinning with delight. "Private Dean's in the fourth day of his fever. It's a light case. He's already on the road to recovery."

Even as he spoke, he could hardly believe his words. The events of this September left him dizzy whenever he thought of them. The first of the series of magnificent telegrams from Lazear had stated that Private William H. Dean, B Company, Sixth Cavalry, had submitted to the bite of an infected mosquito and that, six days later, he had been taken to the isolation wards at Camp Columbia. His illness had been diagnosed by Lazear, Agramonte, Captain A. N. Stark, and Dr. Roger Post Ames as yellow fever.

Lazear's message had been brief. But his words had crackled with pleasure. Lazear had pointed out that Dean had never before suffered from the fever and that he had not been in contact with it for a period of at least two months. There could be no mistaking the fact that, for the first time since Finlay had advanced his theory 19 years ago, a mosquito had succeeded in producing a laboratory case of yellow jack. The death knell of yellow fever had been sounded.

In the following days, telegrams had been fired back and forth between Washington and Camp Columbia. Reed wanted daily reports on Dean's progress through the disease, and he got them. He requested Lazear and Agramonte to check again into Dean's background to make double sure that the soldier had never suffered an attack of yellow fever as a boy. The reply came back immediately; yellow fever was nowhere to be found in the soldier's army medical record, and Dean himself had said, "Well, Doc, if I ever had the yellow jack, it sure didn't feel like this." Reed then asked that a double check be made on Dean's movements for the past two months. Hours later he received a message stating that Agramonte had gone over to B Company, Seventh Cavalry, and had questioned Dean's superior officers closely. They had all stated that there had been no fever in B Company or in those companies surrounding it for two months. The message added that Dean had not been out of the camp for that two months.

All through the four days that they had exchanged messages, Reed had prayed for Lazear. In not one of his messages did Lazear reveal his emotional state, but Reed knew what it well must be. Jesse now thought that he had given two men the yellow fever. In the moment of triumph for his cherished mosquito theory, he must be looking on himself as a possible murderer.

Now had come the finest message of all. Dean was on the road to recovery and . . .

Reed heard General Sternberg speak the very name that was on his own mind.

"And Carroll? How is Carroll?"

"He's fine, sir. Definitely recovering."

A great wave of relief poured through Reed. One of his happiest moments had come that morning when he had wired Mrs. Carroll at her home: "James definitely improving. Lazear confident of full recovery. I know how happy you must feel at this time. My love to you and the children."

He told Sternberg what he had never dared to write Mrs. Carroll. "It was touch-and-go for a time. Lazear thought

[*121*]

they were going to lose him. But he's got more than his share of spirit. He's coming out of it just fine."

Sternberg nodded. "Good. Good. I'm very happy for you. I know how close you are to Carroll." The Surgeon General's face now became serious. "And so your Commission seems to have the yellow fever problem well in hand. This is fine news. Fine news."

"Well, at least, sir, we're on our way to having it under control."

"But you now have two cases which you know were caused by the mosquito."

"One case actually, sir," Reed corrected him. "As you know, we must discount Carroll's attack. He might have picked up the fever from any one of a number of sources. But Dean's case. It's conclusive. We'll have to work from there."

"What steps do you intend to take?"

"First, we both know that a great segment of the medical world is not going to accept Finlay's theory after just one experiment. There are thousands of doctors who will not easily give up their belief in the fomites. I should know; I was one of them for a long while. They're going to want more proof before they change their ideas." He dropped his eyes. His hands worked nervously at the telegram. "I'm afraid we're going to have to give it to them."

Sternberg's voice was low. "You plan to pass the fever into more men?" He was as much filled with detestation over this idea as was Reed. He had been openly shocked when he had first learned that Reed was permitting Lazear to use human guinea pigs.

[*122*]

"Is there any other way, sir?"

The general shook his head. "No. Unfortunately."

"I hope," Reed said, "to be able to work out some demonstration that will do two things at once—conclusively prove the mosquito idea and conclusively disprove the fomites theory."

"I wish you luck," Sternberg said. He stared up at the ceiling. "Any ideas?"

"Not a one as yet," Reed confessed.

"If I know you, Major," Sternberg said, "you'll think of something." He straightened in the chair and leaned toward Reed. "And now for your second problem. It concerns the ten men, including Lazear, who took the bites of infected mosquitoes last month. Right?"

"Very right."

Sternberg shook his head in wonder. "What fools I thought they were. What silly, brave fools."

Reed mused, "Not one of those men fell ill. And yet, Carroll and Dean are both down with the fever. We're going to have to find out why ten men did not become ill when the other two did. If we don't, I'm afraid all the doubters in the medical profession are going to insist that Carroll's and Dean's attacks were simply mistakes and that they had nothing to do with the mosquito."

"You're taking on a tall order for yourself. Even Lazear, who actually conducted the experiment, hasn't been able to find the answer."

"I intend to go over his notes with him when I return to Havana," Reed said. "With a fresh eye, I may be able to see something that he has missed. And, General, I should like to get back to Cuba as soon as possible. With your permission, I'll leave just as soon as the typhoid report is complete. It should be done in about two weeks."

"By all means. I'll have your travel orders waiting for you when you're ready."

Reed was now on his feet, impatient to get on with his work, impatient to be aboard a ship heading south. Sternberg stood up and walked him to the door. "Well, I can't blame you. I only wish that I were going along with you." He extended his hand. "Walter, my congratulations. You've done a wonderful thing with this yellow fever business."

Reed shook his head. "Thank you, sir, but I can't accept the credit. It has to go to Lazear and Carroll and Agramonte. They were on the scene all during the time that the real work was being done."

"It must have been hard to sit up here while all that was going on," Sternberg said.

"I must confess that it was."

"Well, get back as soon as you can. There's much work yet to be done."

"Thank you, sir."

Sternberg pulled the door open. He looked thoughtful for a moment. Then he said, "I wonder if you would do me a favor when you return to Havana?"

"Certainly, sir. What is it?"

"When you see Finlay, apologize to him for me. I—I'm one of the many doctors who has done him a grave injustice all these years. I'm one of the ones who doubted him."

As the door closed behind him, Reed heard Sternberg murmur with wonder,

"Mosquitoes. Mosquitoes."

Reed walked back to his office, sat down at his desk, and luxuriated in his happiness. He remembered his feelings as he had stood on the ship leaving Havana, and he was astonished at how accurately his emotions had foreshadowed the future. Carroll's illness had been the coming disaster he had sensed. But now all was well. They had taken the first step toward conclusive proof of the mosquito theory. Carroll and Dean were on the road to recovery.

He did not know it, but he was eight days away from tragedy.

Agramonte slowly put the telephone receiver back on the hook. He stared at the instrument for a long moment, his face blank. He had the dizzying sensation that he was asleep and that he was dreaming the same dream again and again. It was September 19th. Just three weeks ago, he had picked up that phone and had heard Lazear say in a tight voice that Carroll was ill. Now, he had heard the voice of Carroll, weak yet with the last remnants of the fever, say, "You'd better come out to Columbia right away. I think Lazear's got it."

Agramonte had been standing at the time. His legs had seemed to go out from under him. He had dropped to the high stool alongside his work table so hard that a dull little pain had started up his spine.

"Are you certain?" he had asked.

"I've had it myself. I ought to know."

"Of course. I'll be right out, Jim."

Agramonte shook himself out of his daze and forced

himself to his feet. He walked woodenly to the coat rack near the door. He took down his tunic and put it on, but his mind was not on his actions. He was thinking that he hated his island country at this moment. It was a place of death.

He walked out of the laboratory and across the hospital grounds to the stable where the wagons were kept. Absent-mindedly, he returned the salute of two passing orderlies. He requisitioned a wagon from the sergeant in charge of the stable and drove out into the streets of Havana.

The city was busy that day. People crowded the side-walks. Carriages and wagons rattled through the rutted streets, spewing dust from under their wheels. Children ran to him begging for candy. A beautiful young woman smiled flirtatiously at him from a passing carriage.

He paid no attention to the hustle and bustle in the streets, to the children, to the smiling young woman. The reins lay slack in his hands. He did not even bother to guide the horse pulling the wagon. The animal knew the route to Columbia as well as he. His mind was on Lazear and the events of the past three days.

In the light of what Carroll had just said on the tele-phone, so many little things that Agramonte had noticed in those days now made sense. The day before Lazear had said, "I must be getting old. I guess all this work is getting me down. I feel a little out of sorts today."

Tiredness was not an unusual thing. Both he and Lazear had managed little more than four hours sleep a night dur-ing September. At first, they had been on their feet, watching Carroll and Dean, doing all they could to pull those two men back to health. They had spent their nights discussing Dr.

Finlay's theory.

Yesterday, he had heard Carroll tell Lazear, "You look like the devil."

And he had heard Lazear reply with a rueful grin, "Carroll, my boy, I *feel* like the devil."

At the time, they had been sitting on the veranda of the officers' quarters, where Carroll was recuperating after his release from the isolation ward. Agramonte had asked, "You're not coming down with the fever, are you?"

Lazear had waved him away. "Don't be silly. We know that the only way you can get the fever is to be bitten by the *Culex fasciatus*. And I haven't been bitten. At least, not *this* month."

"You haven't been experimenting on yourself again, have you?" Carroll had asked in a tight voice.

"Of course not. You know that the Commission ruled that we shouldn't allow ourselves to be bitten."

They had accepted his reply and had said no more. But now Agramonte thought about that reply.

Since when had Lazear ever paid any attention to such rules? He had experimented on himself just last month. "Well," Agramonte thought grimly, "We'll soon find out if he was telling the truth or not."

The wagon pulled into Camp Columbia a little over an hour later. Agramonte reined to a halt below the veranda of the officers' quarters. Carroll, who had been seated there, came slowly down the steps. Out of the isolation ward for a week now, he was still unsteady. He had lost much weight; his clothes hung on him as though they were gifts from a circus giant. His face was the color of chalk. His eyes were still red-rimmed.

"Where is he?" Agramonte asked.

"Upstairs." Carroll said.

"Let's have a look at him."

They mounted the steps to Lazear's second story room. Agramonte pushed open the door without knocking. Lazear lifted his head at the sight of the two men and attempted to wave jauntily. The blinds were drawn, but Agramonte could see the deep yellow in his face. The Cuban knew then what Carroll had known for hours: Lazear was down with the yellow jack.

Agramonte moved swiftly to the bedside.

"Good morning, Jesse," he said flatly. "Why did you lie to us the day before yesterday?"

"What are you talking about?"

"Why did you say you hadn't been experimenting with the mosquitoes?"

"I hadn't."

"The devil you haven't. There's no other way you could have picked this up. Or are you trying to convince us that the fomites can still spread the fever."

Lazear attempted a laugh. "You win, Aristides. I'll tell you what happened."

Carroll, still standing in the doorway, snorted with anger and muttered, "You blasted fool. You should have known better."

Agramonte waved him to silence. "He's going to the hospital right now."

Carroll nodded. He took a weak step out into the hall. "Orderly! Orderly!" he shouted.

A soldier arrived breathlessly at Carroll's side. "Yes, sir?"

"Get a couple of stretcher bearers. On the double. Dr. Lazear's going to the hospital."

"Is it the fever, sir?"

"Yes," Carroll said savagely. "It's the fever! Now shake a leg, boy."

The orderly disappeared. Carroll came back into the room, his pale face hard with anger. He glared down at Lazear.

"All right! Let's have it straight. When did you let one of your mosquitoes bite you?"

It had been an accident, Lazear had insisted in a weak voice. He had thought nothing of it at the time.

Five days before, about halfway through his feeding rounds at Las Animas, he had stopped at a bed just inside the door of Number 3 ward, the bed of Corporal Leonard Wilson, New York City. Case: five days old. Condition: serious. But on the mend. . . .

"Good morning, Wilson."

The voice that answered him was low and hoarse. "Morning, Doc. You back again?"

"It looks that way. How about giving one of my "birds" her breakfast?"

Wilson's yellow face nodded. "Why not? You going to give somebody else the fever from me—through the mosquito?"

"Just as soon as I can."

Groaning a little, Wilson brought his arms from beneath the blanket that covered him. "Okay. Maybe it'll do some good."

"I'm sure it will. It's done some good already. You've heard about Private Dean, haven't you?"

"Sure. Who hasn't? How's he doing?"

"Right as rain. He's fine, just as you're going to be."

"I hope so, Doc. I truly hope so," Wilson said.

Lazear selected a test tube and lowered it, upside down, to Wilson's arm. As he did so, he heard a buzzing sound near his ear. For a moment he thought his mosquito had escaped. He blinked and saw that the mosquito was there, clinging to the glass wall. Wilson laughed hoarsely and said: "We got company, Doc. Think it wants breakfast, too?"

The buzzing sound swept close to Lazear's ear again. Then he saw the cause of it, a small brown mosquito. It came to rest where the blanket humped over Wilson's chest. The patient raised his head. With his free hand, he attempted a tired slap at the insect, but the brown mosquito adroitly whirled away from under the shadow of his lowering hand.

Lazear said, "Hold still, boy. You almost knocked the tube off your arm."

"Sorry, Doc. But I don't like them things."

"I can't say I blame you."

There was silence for awhile, and Lazear thought that the insect had flown out through the door. He forgot about it and gave his full attention to the test tube. The "bird" within still clung to the glass tube. Lazear clicked it with his fingernail. He grunted with pleasure when the mosquito skipped away and circled down to Wilson's arm.

The buzzing sounded again. The brown visitor swooped past Lazear's ear, executed a few dizzying circles in front of the doctor's eyes, and then landed on the back of the hand that held the test tube.

Lazear regarded the mosquito angrily. He knew he was going to be bitten, but he did not dare strike the insect for fear of upsetting the test tube. He decided that he need not bother. Let it have a meal if it wished. He didn't think it was a *Culex fasciatus*. He felt the mosquito dig its needle-like beak into his skin. The bite stung. After a while, the mosquito flew away.

Lazear looked at the ugly little welt rising on the back of his hand.

No matter, he thought.

Carroll, standing at the foot of Lazear's bed, heard the story through to the end. His angry breath whistled in the silence that followed. For the first time in days, there was color in his face. His mouth was strung out in a thin line of disgust.

Finally he spoke, harshly. "Do you really expect us to swallow that yarn?"

The effort of telling the story had exhausted Lazear. His head fell to one side of the pillow so that his face was toward Agramonte. He swallowed hard, making a popping sound deep in his throat.

"You've got no choice but to believe it."

"The devil I do!" Carroll said. He shuffled around to the side of the bed so that he would not miss a single expression in Lazear's face. He gestured at Agramonte. "I don't believe it and neither does Aristides. You've been working with the *Culex fasciatus* for weeks now. Every day and every night. But you say you didn't *think* it was a *Culex fasciatus* that bit you. Are you trying to tell us that you can't recognize one at a glance?"

"That's exactly what I'm saying," Lazear said. His eyes were closed. A narrow, glistening stream of sweat ran across his cheek.

Carroll bent down to him. "You mean to say that you didn't notice whether it had stripes across the back? You didn't notice that simple little detail?"

Lazear lifted a hand and pushed it against Carroll's shoulders. He turned suddenly in the bed, groaning as he did so, and rolled over on his left side, taking his eyes away from the men watching him, cutting himself off completely from them.

Carroll stared at him for a long moment. Then his shoulders sagged. He extended his hand and closed it over Lazear's arm.

"I'm sorry, old man. I didn't mean to lose my temper."

As if from very faraway, Lazear said, "Forget it."

Lazear knew that he was swinging back and forth between two worlds, the world of reality and the wild world of delirium. Both were filled with pain.

When he was in the world of reality, he knew that he was lying in a narrow bed in one of the fever wards and that Carroll and Agramonte were staring down at him. He was able to talk coherently with his two friends and answer their questions. He could look directly into their frightened eyes and insist that he had found the fever by accident. He was able to grin and say that now they had three cases of yellow jack to substantiate Finlay's theory.

But, when the wild universe of delirium closed over him, he knew that the fever would carry him wherever it chose. Once, he seemed to be on the road to Havana. He was carrying his little tray of test tubes to Las Animas Hospital for the round of feedings, and he was in a great hurry. The mosquitoes had not been fed for days now, and they were dying of starvation. Tears were running down his cheeks; he was lifting his legs and thrusting them out in front of him, but the road was not moving underfoot. A great weight seemed to be pushing down on him, filling his arms and legs and back with an excrutiating pain. He knew that he was being pressed down into the ground, and he wanted to look upward to see what it was that was pressing him down. But he knew that he should not look up; he knew that looming above him was something horrible. He tried to stop the movement of his eyes, but he could not control them. They swung upward and he was staring straight into the sun. He screamed, for the sun, scorching him with its terrible heat, was descending on him, dancing crazily, filling his head with flashing lights and finally swallowing him.

Oddly enough, as the days went by, he came to prefer the wild universe of delirium to the world of reality. During those moments when his mind was crystal clear, he was able to assess his own condition just as he had been able to assess the conditions of other patients in the past. He knew that his temperature had risen to over 104 degrees. He was able to gauge the depth of his illness by the severity of the pains that wracked his body. He knew enough not to be calm when he entered the "period of calm," that time when the fever seemed to abandon his body. He knew that this was only a passing stage and that, if he were as seriously ill as he reckoned, the febrile reaction would soon set in.

Just as he had anticipated, the febrile reaction took place, and he lived for hours suspended in a void of pain. In one minute, his entire body would be raging with a sort of invisible flame. Sweat would pour out of him and his mouth would go dry, so dry that he could hardly call out for a drink of water. In the next moment, he would be shivering with an intolerable cold. The perspiration would chill on him and his yellowed skin would prickle over with thousands of tiny lumps. Finally, he would be taken off into the world of delirium, a blessed world by this time.

As the fever advanced into the fourth week of September, he thought less and less of himself during his lucid moments. He hated the idea of not being able to continue with his work. The Commission was just a hair's breadth away from total success. But he was happy for the part he had played in that work. He knew he had made a real contribution to medical science. He knew that he was partly responsible for creating a future in which there would be less pain. What more could a doctor ask for?

About his family he felt only regret, regret that he had not seen them in such a long time. He wondered if his wife had finished sewing the dress she had mentioned in her last letter. He wondered how big his children had grown and if the younger one was walking yet. He wondered how they were going to get along after he. . . .

All that was human in him told him that he was not going to die. He was going to live. He was going to work

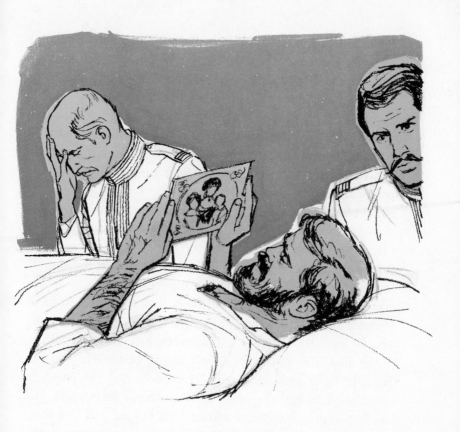

Lazear saw his family as he had never seen them before.

again. He was going to be with his family again. The doctor
that was in him laughed dryly.

He asked Carroll to bring from his room a photograph
of his wife and children. When he felt Carroll press it into his
hands, he lifted it up and gazed at it for a long time. He saw
the three figures through a haze of yellow. He had always
thought that they had looked very stiff in that photograph

and that his wife's smile had been artificial. But, now through the haze, the figures seemed soft and rounded. As he gazed at them, they became more real to him than Carroll standing above the bed. He looked at them, and he tried to speak to them of practical things. He mumbled that they would be all right without him. There would undoubtedly be some sort of service pension for them. And there was the insurance. He had always been very careful about the insurance. Suddenly, he could no longer see the figures. They were blurred behind a watery haze.

In the afternoon of the seventh day of the fever, he came slowly back to the world of reality. He lay very still, thinking that the universe of delirium had treated him kindly today. It had caught him up in a soft, warm dream in which everything was perfect. He had been back at Johns Hopkins, working on a research project, and it had been going extremely well. He had gone home and he had done all of those things that a man should do about the house. He had sat down to table with his family. He had carried the children up to bed and had romped with them for a long while. He had come back downstairs and had sat talking with his wife while she sewed. They had talked, he remembered, far into the night.

He slowly opened his eyes. The room came gradually into focus, and he felt the hardness of the mattress. He saw Carroll and Agramonte at the foot of the bed. All the pain and all the heat of yellow jack came back into him.

He felt something press into his shoulder and shake him gently. Anger stirred in him. He wanted to be left alone to find the dream. He pulled his eyes open and saw Carroll bending over him. Carroll's face was cracked with fear.

Carroll's words came at him from a great distance. This surprised him because Carroll was so near. "Jesse! Jesse! Come on, lad, snap out of it!"

He stared up at Carroll and tried to smile. The muscles in his face would not work.

Carroll's head swung to the side so that his whole hawk-like profile blotted out the entire room.

"Agramonte! I think he's going. . . ."

Carroll's words should have frightened him. He knew what they meant. But he didn't care. Slowly, very slowly, he closed his eyes. He was going back to the dream.

The last thing he heard was Carroll's choking sob.

Reed sat down heavily at his desk. With great care he placed the telegram on the blotter. The words on the yellow sheet turned him icy cold.

What had happened was impossible. Lazear could not be dead. The telegram was a horrible mistake. Lazear had too much vitality to die. Lazear had too much to offer the world. There was so much more that he was going to do when the battle with yellow fever was done. He—

Something inside Reed cracked. He leaned forward and put his face in his hands. His shoulders heaved convulsively. He might have been crying for a dead son.

Chapter 10

Discovery

Walter Reed came back to Cuba on October 4, his face gray and drawn, but no longer with grief. He had done all his mourning in Washington. There was sorrow within yet, but he had pushed it to one side so that it would not get in the way of what he had to do to destroy the yellow fever. Nothing must hinder the avenging of Jesse Lazear's death.

Reed had always hated the fever, ever since the first day he had studied it. But he had hated it the way any doctor hates a disease, coldly and dispassionately. Now he felt a different sort of hate, much deeper, more intense. He did not know of any word that could adequately describe it.

He only knew that the fever had killed a man whom he had come to think upon as a son. It had killed a brilliant, vital man that the world sorely needed. He was determined to wipe out that killer. If necessary, he would spend the rest of his life at the job.

Agramonte met him at dockside. Together, they rode out to Camp Columbia. From Agramonte, the Major heard again the story of Lazear's death. It was far more horrible hearing a human voice tell it than it had been reading it in the telegram and the letters that had followed.

The wagon pulled up in front of the officers' quarters. Reed watched Carroll come down the steps to greet him, and he felt in his heart another reason for loathing the fever as he did. Carroll's attack was more than a month old, and the man was so far along the road to recovery that—according to Agramonte—he had recently performed an autopsy or two. But many months would pass, Reed knew, before Carroll got back his full strength. He was thin and pale. His eyes showed the exhaustion that was still in him. Reed decided that Carroll must be sent home on leave in the next week.

The three doctors sat talking on the veranda for a while. For the second time that day, Reed heard the story of Lazear's passing. Carroll, he saw, was also deeply upset by the death. He and Lazear had often stood on opposite sides in their beliefs of how the fever was spread. Reed recalled how heatedly they had argued during the first meeting of the Commission. But they had survived that argument and had become good friends, filled with respect for each other.

In the long moment of silence after Carroll had finished his story, Reed leaned far forward in his chair. "I don't understand it," he said. "I just don't understand it."

"What is that, sir?" Agramonte asked.

"I don't understand how Lazear failed to recognize the mosquito that bit him. He'd worked so long with the *Culex fasciatus*. He should have identified it at a glance."

He looked up in time to see Agramonte and Carroll exchange a sharp glance. He understood the meaning behind that glance.

"So you've suspected the same thing?"

Agramonte, after an assenting nod from Carroll, said, "Yes, sir."

Reed felt himself begin to tremble. "You think that he was experimenting on himself?"

"Frankly, Major," Carroll spoke up, "We don't see any other answer."

"But why," Reed cried, "should he hide that fact from us?"

"We had agreed after you left not to experiment on ourselves. We didn't think that we would do the study any benefit if we were sick."

"Perfectly correct. But that can't be the answer," Reed said. "Lazear experimented on himself in August, several weeks after you had made that ruling."

"We agree. It's definitely not the answer," Agramonte said quietly. "We've gone through Jesse's notebooks—"

"Yes?" Reed leaned forward eagerly.

Agramonte pressed his hands together and regarded them thoughtfully. "Ordinarily, Jesse kept very thorough and very concise sets of notes on all his work."

"But," Carroll broke in, "you should see the last pages in his notebook, the pages that cover the two weeks before he fell ill. They don't look as if they were written by the same man. They're vague. Sketchily written. And there are short notations that make no sense at all. I'm willing to bet my last dollar that he was trying to cover up experiments performed on himself. In case anything happened to him, he didn't want anyone to read that book and learn what he had actually done."

"But why? Why would he do that?"

"We can only guess," Agramonte said. "But we think our guess is a pretty good one. Lazear carried a great deal of insurance on his family. It's obvious that he didn't think of it when he allowed himself to be bitten the first time. But he must have thought of it later, when he was ready to be bitten again."

"I see," Reed said. "He must have thought that his insurance would be taken away from his family if it were ever learned that he had deliberately exposed his life to a deadly disease. The idea of his wife and children being left without any means of support if he died must have appalled him."

Reed stopped in front of the veranda screen. He stared out at the patch of green-brown lawn. Jesse, Jesse, he thought. You brave fool. Why did you have to take your own life in your hands? You could have found others to take your place. You're needed so badly here.

Reed felt tears start up into his eyes. He spoke softly, hoarsely, without looking back at Agramonte and Carroll.

"If that is the case, gentlemen, then I think we should keep Lazear's confidence. Let his family live in what peace they can find. I suggest that we never talk about this matter again. As far as we are concerned, Jesse Lazear died of an accidental bite from the mosquito *Culex fasciatus.*" He swallowed, feeling the tears well over his lower lids. "Agreed?"

Agramonte and Carroll said, "Agreed."

Reed stood where he was for another moment. He forced

the tears back. He remembered his promise never to let his emotions get in the way of the work that he had to do on Jesse's behalf. His eyes were dry and his voice firm when he turned back to Carroll and Agramonte. "We can talk long of Jesse, for we all loved and admired him. But all the talk in the world won't bring him back and won't solve this yellow fever business. Aristides, I want you to come with me to Jesse's laboratory. You, too, Jim, if you feel up to it."

"Of course I feel up to it," Carroll said.

Reed came back to the chairs. "Before we can advance our studies and remove all doubt concerning Finlay's theory, there is one task that must be gotten out of the way."

Agramonte smiled. "We know the job you mean, sir. Carroll and I have talked about it several times. We've got to learn why he and Dean and then Lazear took sick from the bite of a mosquito after the ten men of the August experiments remained perfectly well."

"Exactly. And I think we'll start to look for that answer in Lazear's notebooks. Perhaps he's left us some clue—"

"But we've already looked at them," Carroll said. "Until we were blue in the face. There isn't a thing there—at least, not that we could see."

The man spoke with such frustration that Reed put a hand on his shoulder. "Well, perhaps, another head on the job will help."

The three officers left the veranda and walked across the hospital grounds to Lazear's laboratory. As he climbed the steps, Reed took a firm grip on his emotions. He breathed deeply and pushed the door of the laboratory open. He could not restrain the gasp that rose to his lips. The room was as

[*143*]

dead as Lazear. Everything was too tidy, too untouched, for the living. Notebooks were stacked neatly at the edge of each work table. Laboratory equipment stood in the soldier-like rows on the shelves. The air in the room was thick and unused. The shutters were drawn, allowing only thin shafts of light to steal in between their slats. Even the dust had a smooth, unruffled look to it.

Agramonte threw open the shutters, letting in the afternoon air, while Carroll gathered Lazear's work books and brought them to a table. The two men came to stand at Reed's side as he selected the latest of the books and opened it to the first page. Lazear's handwriting, bringing the memory of the man sharply into focus, sprang up from the page.

For close to an hour the three men stood over the notebook. The thoroughness and precision of Lazear's work amazed Reed. Here, in neat columns, was the complete record of Jesse's August researches. Each mosquito was designated by a number. Listed, day by day, were the names of the fever victims on whom the mosquitoes had fed. Alongside each name was a notation on the length of time the patient had been ill. Towards the middle of the book Reed came upon the records of the ten men who had submitted to the bites of the infected mosquitoes. Lazear had not failed to insert his own record among them.

Neat as the figures were, they maddened Reed. As Carroll had said, they gave no clue to the problem troubling them. Reed broke away from the table and strode up and down the laboratory, feeling the need for some sort of movement to clear his fogged brain.

"I'm hanged if I can find a thing to help us," he said,

adding in desperation, "Read some of the data on the feedings aloud, Aristides. Perhaps it will help if I can hear rather than see it."

"Yes, sir," Agramonte said.

With his chin cupped in his hand, the Cuban began to recite:

"Feedings—August 10: Mosquito four—Private Lester Haley—case: six days advanced. Mosquito five—Sergeant Adam Appleby—case: four days advanced. Mosquito six—Lieutenant Andrew Hardesty—case: seven days advanced. Mosquito seven—Sergeant Philip Manley—case: four days advanced."

Agramonte, growing impatient, flipped over several pages, coming at last to rest on the sheet dated August 15. "Mosquito twelve." He shot an amused glance at Carroll. "Isn't that the little beast that gave you and Dean the fever?"

"Yes."

"Well, this must be a record of his first feeding. Look. August 15: Mosquito twelve—Private William Jameson—case: two days advanced."

Carroll nodded. "That's our girl, all right. Lazear told me that she had taken her first feeding twelve days before she bit me. I was bitten on the 27th, if you remember."

"How can I forget it?"

Reed was at the far end of the room, staring out the window. Suddenly he stiffened and whirled about. He spoke so sharply that both Agramonte and Carroll jumped with surprise. "What did you say?"

Agramonte looked flustered for a moment. "I was just telling Carroll that I'd not likely ever forget the 27th—"

[145]

Reed stepped quickly toward the table, gesturing impatiently. "No. No. Before that. Something about the mosquito being fed on August 15. Read it again."

"August 15: Mosquito twelve—Private William Jameson—case: two days old."

Agramonte looked up to see a smile of triumph spread over Reed's face. It was the first time that he had seen the man smile today. Reed snatched up the notebook. He stared down at Lazear's strong, neat handwriting. Then, while his two companions regarded him as if he had lost his mind, he went from page to page through the entire August record. He studied every column of names and dates, not once, not twice, but three times. His whole being was flashing with excitement when he finally looked up.

"That's it! That's it! It's got to be the answer!"

"What on earth are you talking about?" came from an exasperated Carroll.

In reply, Reed thrust the notebook at him. "Here! Look for yourself. Read any page carefully. Then check it against the feeding record of mosquitoes. And then tell me what you see. Tell me!"

The two puzzled doctors did as they were told. Agramonte was the first to understand. His dark head shot up, and he turned blazing eyes on Reed.

"Yes, yes, I see! It was there for us all the while. And we just didn't have the eyes for it!"

Carroll shook his head. He was leaning against the table, supporting himself by the palms of his hands. His hawk-like face was tight with concentration, as he stared down at the page recording the August 15th feeding of Mosquito twelve.

For the life of him, he could not fathom what Reed and Agramonte had seen.

Finally, Reed could no longer restrain himself. He jabbed a finger down hard on the page.

"Jim, the mosquito that bit you and Dean had fed on a fever patient that was only *two days* advanced into his case. All the other feedings for the month were done on cases advanced four, five, six, and seven days."

Now it was Carroll's turn to raise suddenly excited eyes to Reed.

"Of course!" The full import of the fact that Reed had found struck him. "That could be the answer to the whole thing!"

"Could be? It *is!*" Reed swung away from the table. His excited steps carried him the full length of the room and back. His words came rapidly. They were softly but intensely spoken, as if he was talking to himself as much as to his fellow doctors.

"The agent that causes yellow fever is *alive* within the patient only during the first two—possibly three—days of the illness. If a mosquito bites the victim during that time, she takes away a lively, active germ. She passes it onto another person, just as she did, Jim, to you and Dean. But—"

Reed paused, collected his thoughts, found just the right words with which to express them, and hurried on.

"But something happens to the germ after the second or third day. Even though it may be destroying the patient's life, it is no longer capable of spreading the disease to another person. The mosquito can bite a patient after the third day as many times as she wishes. She will carry away no active germ with which to contaminate other people. That's the only explanation that will account for the fact that the ten men bitten during August did not fall ill."

His eyes shining, he gazed from doctor to doctor. He waited eagerly for their reaction to his remarks. They had to believe that what he said was the truth. It was so simple and so logical that it *had* to be truth. He breathed a sigh of relief when Agramonte, slapping the table with the flat of his hand, cried,

"That's it, Major! It's perfect. All the pieces fit together into a beautiful pattern."

Reed nodded, then swung his eyes to Carroll. "Well, Jim, what do you think?"

Carroll passed a hand across his forehead. He was still too weak to be able to think as quickly as his two companions.

"I need a little time. A little time. But it seems right. It seems to make sense."

Reed came round the work table and slapped him on the shoulder. "Indeed it makes sense! Believe me, Jim, we've solved one part of the problem."

Agramonte's dark brows shot up. "One part?"

"Yes." Reed's mind was moving at lightning pace now. He picked up the notebook. "There's something else that struck me here. Jim, you were bitten on the 27th of August."

"Yes."

"And Dean on the 31st?"

"Yes."

"And on August 15th your mosquito had fed from a patient who had been sick two days with the fever?"

"Yes. What are you driving at?"

[*148*]

Reed held up his hand, holding off momentarily his answer. He thumbed through the notebook, checking the pages on which were listed the names of the ten men who had submitted to the bites of the infected *Culex fasciatus*. As he read through their names and records, he said,

"Just a moment ago, I remembered something that Jesse told me back in July. He said that a Doctor Henry R. Carter of the Marine Service had discovered something about the fever during a recent epidemic in Mississippi. He found that, after the first case of fever appeared in a neighborhood, some two to three weeks had to pass before the second case appeared. After that, the fever required a week to show up.

His voice trailed away as he studied the names and dates. When he was done, he struck the page with his knuckles.

"Another fact fallen right into place!"

Carroll shook his head. The Major had lost him again. He smiled ruefully. "Now, suppose you let us in on it."

Reed held the book out to him. "Look. Everyone of the men was bitten by mosquitoes that had fed on a patient no more than three days before. Look. Right here at the top of the page. 'August 18: This day Private Julius Howard was bitten by Mosquito seven, which took its last feeding (from Private Lawrence Higgins) on August 16'." Reed flipped to another page. "And here. 'August 19: Today Manuel Machado, a Cuban, was bitten by Mosquito nine. Mosquito nine was fed on August 16 from patient, Sergeant Alfred Blake. Machado thought that taking the bite was a great joke.'"

Reed snapped the book shut. "It's the same all the way through. No more than two or three days passed between the time that a mosquito fed on a patient and the time that she bit one of our ten men." He gripped Carroll's arm and shook it in his excitement. "Only you and Dean were bitten by a mosquito that had not been fed that recently. When you were bitten, 12 days had passed since the mosquito had been fed; 16 days before she got onto Dean."

He saw that neither Agramonte nor Carroll as yet saw the connection between Carter's observations in Mississippi and the length of time between feeding and experimental bites of Mosquito three.

He explained slowly, "Carter believes that the fever is spread by some sort of insect. He feels that the two to three weeks that pass between the first and second cases in a district can be accounted for by the fact that the germ of the fever is growing in strength inside the insect. The germ is not strong enough to harm anyone who is bitten until that time period elapses. It looks as though he is absolutely right!"

Reed sat down suddenly. He felt very tired. It seemed to him that never in all his life had he taxed his brain as much as he had in the last few minutes. Savoring the result of his thinking, he went back over all that he had said, summarizing for his benefit and that of his listeners.

"The whole secret of the spread of yellow fever is bound up in two little facts. First, the mosquito must bite the fever victim in the first two or three days of his illness; that is the time when the germ of the fever is in its active state. After the fourth day, the germ has lost its power to infect another person. Second, once the mosquito has bitten the patient, the germ of the disease must grow within the mosquito until it is powerful enough to harm another person. That growth requires approximately twelve days."

He sighed with satisfaction as he looked from face to face and saw each of the doctors nod.

A deep silence settled over the room. Agramonte and Carroll stared at Reed with open admiration, though they did not speak, for they knew the modest, gray haired man would be embarrassed by the things they wanted to say. Here in this laboratory, on a treeless slope in Cuba, a U.S. medical officer had solved a puzzle that had bewildered the scientific world for some 250 years. It was an accomplishment that would earn him enduring fame in the annals of medicine.

Reed stirred himself from his own thoughts. He stood up.

"And now, gentlemen, we have some work to do. I want to talk to you about a plan I've work out. If it works, the world will be done with yellow fever once and for all.

Chapter 11

Camp Lazear

Reed's plan for the destruction of yellow fever was divided into three parts. He had carefully worked them out while still in Washington, and now he explained them to Carroll and Agramonte.

"They're designed not only to destroy yellow fever but to knock out some of the myths that surround it," he said. The men followed him out onto the veranda of the laboratory. The sun was low in the horizon flooding the grounds of Columbia with a blood red light. "Now, this is what I have in mind."

Reed breathed in the cooling air and explained that, first, the Commission would attempt to infect more men with yellow fever from the bites of infected mosquitoes. It was a filthy job, one that he looked upon with loathing. But it was a job that had to be done. The scientific world would never accept Finlay's theory without conclusive proof.

Second, Reed continued, the Commission had to prove

that fomites had nothing to do with the spread of the fever. In addition to verification, Finlay's theory needed to see the fomites theory destroyed.

"The third part of the plan brings us right back to where the Commission started," Reed said. "We're going after the cause of the fever. We've never been able to find the germ responsible for yellow jack."

He saw Agramonte and Carroll grin. They were remembering those terrible days and nights of June and July.

"Perhaps in our lifetime," he said, "it will not be found. Perhaps investigators years from now will come on it." But, he continued, the Commission was at least going to put those investigators on the right track. It was going to get as close to the germ as possible. It was going to attempt to prove to the world that the germ was to be found in the blood stream, where doctors had long suspected it resided. "Well," Reed said, "that's the plan. What do you think of it?"

Agramonte answered for both Carroll and himself. "I think it's excellent. We'd best get started on it immediately."

It was an excellent plan, Reed thought as he moved down the laboratory steps with the two doctors. It would be carried out under the strictest controls to prevent any chance of infection from outside sources, and its results would be checked, in turn, by the Havana Yellow Fever Board, whose membership included Doctors Carlos Finlay and William Crawford Gorgas. There was just one problem. Like all good plans, it required money to carry it out.

To solve that problem, Reed traveled to the headquarters in Havana of Brigadier General Leonard N. Wood, the U.S. military governor. He explained what his Commission had thus far accomplished and what it intended to do. He saw Wood's expression glow in wonder as the story of Lazear and the eventual pinpointing of the responsibility of yellow fever on the *Culex fasciatus* unfolded. At the end of his story, he requested sufficient funds to put his plan into action.

For two reasons, Reed fully expected to receive help from Wood. First, in his younger days, the General had studied under Reed at the Army Medical School and had always shown great affection for his teacher. Second, like George Sternberg back up in Washington, the military governor was as much scientist as he was soldier.

When Reed had concluded his appeal for money, Wood leaned his great arms on his desk and asked, "How much do you need, Major?"

Reed had carefully estimated his expenses. "I think $10,000 will be sufficient."

Wood did not bat an eye. "And exactly how do you propose to spend it?"

"Basically, in two ways."

Reed explained that he did not wish to carry out his plan at Columbia. To insure absolute success and to remove all doubt concerning its validity, the plan had to be executed under the strictest controls, away from all possible contact with the fever. Reed hoped to establish a laboratory camp in some secluded spot on the island.

"It will be a rather special camp, General. We'll need a certain kind of building in addition to tents and laboratory facilities."

"I see," Wood said. "Go on."

Then, Reed explained, it was necessary first to continue

the attempts to induce the fever in humans via the *Culex fasciatus*. If possible, he wished to avoid using Americans in this matter, mainly to avoid criticism at home that might put the whole plan in jeopardy. He thought that many Spaniards who were immigrating to Cuba in increasing numbers war might be induced to take the necessary bites if there was a reward involved—say, $100. After all, when they came to Cuba, they fully expected to contract yellow fever sooner or later. They might as well be reimbursed for coming down with the disease.

Wood heard him out. He pushed his big bulk up from his chair and walked to the window in the rear wall of his office. He stared down at the streets of Havana. In his deep, grumbling voice, he said, "You shall have your $10,000. I'll assign it to you from military government funds." He swung round and grinned at Reed. "And, Major, when you need more, come and see me again."

Reed smiled broadly in return. He came to his feet. "You may count on *that*, sir."

With the problem of money settled, Reed turned his attention to other matters. He sent Carroll home to the states on leave. He wanted him in the best of health when the plan actually went into effect. He gave Agramonte the job of keeping Lazear's mosquitoes alive and well fed, and ordered him to search for a suitable site for the proposed camp. Then Reed himself returned to the United States for two weeks.

He went home not to rest but to bring to doctors the news of the last victories against the yellow death. On October 24, at a meeting of the American Public Health Association at Indianapolis, he presented that news. In a short paper, assembled from Lazear's notes and entitled "Preliminary Note," he announced the Commission's success in inducing through the mosquito *Culex fasciatus* a case of yellow fever in an American soldier. He stated that, though one laboratory case was meager scientific evidence, there was every reason to believe that the problem of how yellow fever was spread was close to its final solution. The Association greeted his words with mixed reactions. On some sides, he was congratulated. On others, he was met with polite skepticism. He returned to Cuba in early November, resolved to win over the skeptics in the shortest time possible.

Back in Cuba, Reed found that Agramonte had investigated several possible sites for the camp and that he recommended one in particular. It was an area of uncultivated land on a farm that belonged to Agramonte's Havana friend, Dr. Ignacio Roja. Reed went out to investigate the site. Immediately, he liked what he saw. The plot of ground was located about a mile outside Quemados. Though secluded, it was just off the Calzada Real, the main road to Camp Columbia. It would be easy to bring supplies there quickly when needed. Drainage was good, and, because the site was unsheltered by trees and open to the wind, it would be free of all mosquitoes except those kept by the Commission.

"This will be it," Reed said at the end of his first visit. "This is where we'll establish Camp Lazear."

Agramonte had not heard the name before. "Camp Lazear?"

"Yes. It seems exactly right. After all, it was Lazear who set us upon the path to the work that—God willing—we will complete here."

The plan for the Infected Clothing Building was a puzzle.

Agramonte nodded slowly. He murmured, "I think Jesse would like that."

A detail of soldiers was brought in to erect the camp. Seven tents, and sanitary facilities were immediately set up. A short distance away from the tents, the Quartermaster Corps began the construction of a small wooden house. They worked according to a set of plans that Reed had given them. The soldier-carpenters looked at the plans and scratched their heads; the building, with hardly proper ventilation, looked positively sinister. Reed agreed with them. The building was sinister. He called it the Infected Clothing Building and said that it was going to be used for the filthiest experiment that a scientist had ever devised. It was going to be used to disprove the fomites theory. He explained how the experiment was to be performed. When he had walked away, the soldier-carpenters looked at each other with disgust.

Before Camp Lazear was ready for occupation, a second building had to be erected. A tropical storm that struck Havana in the second week of November plunged the temperature to the low 60's. Dr. Finlay, at his initial meeting with the Commission, had warned that the fragile *Culex fasciatus* could not stand cold, windy weather. Reed now recognized the truth of his words. An alarming number of the mosquitoes perished in the laboratories at Columbia and Hospital Number One.

Reed and Agramonte immediately designed a building in which the mosquitoes could be safely housed in a warm temperature. At Agramonte's suggestion, the building was so designed that it could also serve as a station in which volunteers could be infected by the *Culex fasciatus*. The little place was soon informally christened the Mosquito Building.

The shortage of mosquitoes caused by the storm was soon solved by a band of soldiers and doctors, led by Major Albert E. Truby of Camp Columbia. They invaded the Quartermaster dump at Quemados and searched among heaps of discarded water buckets. They returned to Reed with enough *Culex fasciatus* eggs to last him for years.

Camp Lazear was formally opened on the morning of November 20. Reed walked through the grounds. Over to his right stood the seven tents in an orderly, military row; a hospital steward, a Medical Corps private, an ambulance driver, and several Americans who had volunteered for the experiments were just now carrying their luggage toward the tents. Off to his left, workmen were still busying themselves with the Infected Clothing Building and the Mosquito House; the little huts were scheduled to be completed within another ten days. Reed's eyes went round the perimeter of the grounds. Out there, already on patrol, were the soldiers— all of them immune to the fever—the small detachment assigned to guard the camp. Moving slowly among them and gathering rocks were a dozen or so Spanish immigrants who had agreed to take the bites of the *Culex fasciatus*.

Reed's mind went over the personnel that had yet to put in an appearance. Dr. Roger Post Ames, who had realized such success with the treatment of yellow fever at Columbia, was to report in this afternoon; he was to be in charge of the camp, leaving Reed, Agramonte, and Carroll free to concentrate on their experiments. Agramonte was coming over from Havana tomorrow. Carroll, recently returned from his leave, had promised to arrive before the end of the week; at the moment, he was at Columbia completing several bacteriological studies.

Reed nodded with satisfaction. All was in readiness for the work ahead. He smiled grimly. At this moment, Camp Lazear looked quite innocent, just another small military installation set down in the middle of nowhere. But, in a very few weeks, he knew, it would be known as the birthplace of some of the harshest medical experiments ever attempted by man.

Chapter 12

Experiments For Mankind

The first part of Reed's plan, the attempt to induce yellow fever through the bite of the *Culex fasciatus*, began at 10:30 in the morning of November 20. One of the Spanish immigrants, summoned from his rock collecting, walked into Reed's tent. There he was joined by John R. Kissinger, private in the Hospital Corps., who, earlier in the week, had volunteered. Each man rolled up his right sleeve, extended his arm, and held it steady while the Major pressed the mouth of a test tube to it, midway between the wrist and the inner curve of the elbow.

The Spaniard and his fellow countrymen had been secured by Agramonte in a somewhat devious manner during the weeks following the agreement made between Reed and General Wood to use immigrants in the experiments. Whenever a ship from Spain made port at Havana, the Cuban doctor, sometimes accompanied by Carroll, went down to

Tiscornia Immigration Station. He strolled among the debarking passengers and hired to work at Camp Lazear eight to ten of the most physically fit of their number. He installed them in tents, gave them mosquito nets for their bunks, fed them, and instructed them to pass their days picking up the countless loose stones that littered the grounds. He mystified them by saying that they were to take their time at the job and that they were to enjoy as many rest periods as they wished.

While they pursued their casual labors, shaking their heads at the unworldly generosity of the United States Army, they were observed closely by Agramonte, Carroll, and Reed and were questioned often concerning their family and medical histories. The doctors paid off and dismissed those who proved not to be so healthy as they had first looked; those who admitted to having previously suffered the yellow jack; and those who had relatives dependent on them.

Then Agramonte assembled those who had survived the trial. He revealed the actual reason for their presence in Camp Lazear. Agramonte explained that he wanted them to submit themselves to the bite of a mosquito, a mosquito that would very likely give them yellow fever; in fact, to be brutally frank, he hoped that it would. He spoke of the danger involved and of the value of the experiment to humanity. He promised them the best of medical care if they fell ill. He later admitted with a grin that he did not mention that the Army would stand the expense of any funerals. He concluded by saying that each man would receive $100 for his trouble, and another $100 if he caught yellow fever.

Their reaction was the expected one. One hundred Yankee dollars! Such a treasure! It was worth any risk. It was just what they needed to establish themselves in style in their new island home. Too, they were of a philosophic turn of mind. In all probability, they were going to come down with the yellow jack anyway; it was always a dangerous possibility when one came to Cuba. So they might as well be paid for having it. They quickly signed the contracts that Agramonte placed before them.

John R. Kissinger had needed no such urging to participate in the work at Camp Lazear. Upon first hearing of Reed's plan, he had gone directly to the Major and had volunteered his services. He was, he had said, just the sort of man Reed could use. He was young—still in his twenties and he was in excellent physical shape. He had known and admired Jesse Lazear. He would deem it an honor to help finish the work which Dr. Lazear had helped begin.

Kissinger's formal presentation of his qualifications had touched Reed. Reed later recalled placing a hand on the young man's shoulder and saying that he would be paid for his courage, though the amount involved could never compensate for the risk he was willing to take. Like the Spaniards, Kissinger was entitled to the reward of $100. Kissinger had politely, but flatly, turned aside the offer. In his own words, he desired only to serve in the interest of humanity and the advancement of science.

Kissinger had soon been joined by other American volunteers. The next was John J. Moran, a civilian clerk with the Army at Havana. The horror and sorrow wrought by yellow fever greatly disturbed him. Like Kissinger, he refused to accept pay for his services.

[*165*]

All in all, Reed ended up with 14 American volunteers. In addition to Kissinger and Moran, Camp Lazear also used the services of the lanky Dr. Robert P. Cook and Hospital Corpsmen Levi E. Folk, Warren G. Jernegan, James Hanberry, Edward Weatherwalks, James Hildebrand, Thomas England, John Andrus, Clyde West, Charles Sonntag, William Olson, and Wallace Forbes.

Outwardly, there was nothing dramatic about the taking of the mosquito bites that morning of November 20. The day was overcast, the interior of Reed's tent gloomy. The Spaniard smiled to himself, thinking of his reward. Kissinger smiled as he extended his arm. And Moran and several other American volunteers, who were being saved for later experiments, watched from the entrance to the tent. They joked with Kissinger, telling him that he looked as though he were actually eager to get the yellow jack. They stopped their talk, however, their eyes narrowing, when they saw the mosquitoes buzzing within the test tubes. Reed, assisted by Dr. Cook, worked swiftly and quietly. He seemed very calm. Had Agramonte and Carroll been present, they would have recognized that calmness for what it was: skin-deep.

Within, Reed was in turmoil. Everything needed to insure perfect control of the experiment seemed well in hand: Agramonte had fed the mosquitoes at just the right time on fever cases of just the right age; the two volunteers had had no contact with fever areas for weeks: both of them were non-immune. Yet Reed was assailed with fears. He dreaded the remote possibility that he had overlooked some small— but very vital—detail. He was half afraid that he was signing the death warrants of two men. He was also half afraid that they would not fall ill and that yellow fever would continue to ravage the world. He knew in his heart that he had come to the greatest days of his career, the days towards which all the years of travel and oftentimes tedious work had constantly pointed. He had the odd feeling that Jesse Lazear was in the room, watching him, nodding approvingly.

. When the bites had been taken, Reed, reviewed the basic rules of the camp. Neither man was to leave the grounds without his permission. The two men would be checked medically several times each day. They were to notify him the very moment they felt ill. He sent the Spaniard back to his rock collecting and his rest periods. He and Kissinger watched the fellow walk away.

Now began the days of waiting, days that Reed lived in an agony of suspense, checking temperatures and pulses, asking after aches and pains, and looking into the faces of his two human guinea-pigs for some sign of a spreading yellowness. There were two unexpected events. One of the Havana newspapers got wind of what was going at Camp Lazear and, on November 21, unleashed a vicious editorial attack against Reed. It has a horrible thing, the paper announced, that this superior and heartless American should so take advantage of poor immigrants, preying on their witlessness and financial need to induce them to gamble their lives for a pittance of $100.

Reed, Carroll, and Agramonte—fearful that the attack would cause diplomatic friction between the United States and Spain that might endanger the work at Camp Lazear—gathered the contracts signed by the laborers and took them to the Spanish consul. They explained the conditions of the

Agramonte desperately counted the unleashed mosquitoes.

experiment, making a special point of saying that they had warned the immigrants of all the dangers involved. The consul nodded with understanding. He, personally, was in favor of any measure, no matter how dangerous, that would put an end to yellow fever. He advised them to ignore the newspaper.

Then, several days later, four infected mosquitoes came close to being unleashed on Havana. One morning Agramonte, riding in a buggy driven by his attendant Private Loud, was transporting mosquitoes from Hospital Number One to the Camp. He had them in test tubes in the pocket inside his tunic. As the buggy rounded a corner on a downgrade near Colon Cemetery, the horse was frightened by a steam roller. Rearing back in terror, the horse then charged down the hill towards the Almenares River. Private Loud disappeared overside at the first bounce. Agramonte struggled with the reins, at the same time trying to hold tight to the precious test tubes. The buggy pitched over on its side, and Agramonte found himself sitting atop a pile of sand in the middle of the road. He gingerly touched his pocket, fully expecting to feel broken bits of glass. He sighed with relief; the tubes were all intact. After he and Private Loud had counted their bruises, they rounded up the horse, quieted him, and proceeded the rest of the way to camp.

By the weekend following the taking of the bites, neither the Spaniard nor Kissinger had fallen ill. The tension accompanying the experiment had worn off, and the other Americans, whose sole duty was to keep their quarters clean, were feeling the first pangs of boredom. The Spaniards went contentedly about their rock collecting and were now building a stone wall along the southern boundary of the camp. Kissinger spent his days in Reed's tent, serving as the Major's secretary, copying letters for him. Agramonte began to fret, wondering if the mosquitoes had been properly fed before being turned loose on the volunteers. Reed, suppressing his own anxiety, put on a calm face and guessed that the cool weather was causing the fever germs to ripen more slowly in the *Culex fasciatus*. It was a good guess.

On that theory, Reed had Kissinger submit himself on November 23 to another bite from the insect that had stung him three days earlier. Moran was next introduced into the experiment. He was bitten on the 26th and 29th of the month. Reed, using all his will power to contain his nervousness, awaited the outcome. The days passed slowly into December. Nothing happened. Reed stared bleakly at his notebook. Was it possible that the experiment was going to fail?

Despite his sagging spirits, on November 30 Reed launched the second phase of his plan: the experiment meant to prove conclusively that fomites did not transmit yellow fever. With Agramonte, Carroll, and three of the American volunteers, he walked over to the Infected Clothing Building at a little past five in the afternoon. His face was pale and set. Indeed, the faces of all the men were colorless. The very thought of what they were about to do filled them with nausea.

The three volunteers were Dr. Cook, Levi E. Folk, and Warren G. Jernegan. When they arrived in front of the one-room building—no more than a shack, really—Reed directed them to enter. Then, followed by Agramonte and Carroll, he went round to the rear wall. He looked in through one of the two small screened windows and saw that the room was in readiness. It was 14 by 20 feet in size. Its walls, two boards thick, were constructed tongue-and-groove. There were only the two small windows, no through ventilation. The room contained three beds, all without bedding. A coal stove stood in a corner. It was burning brightly. The shack was hot and humid, simulating the sort of weather that the yellow jack seemed to love. The temperature stood at 90 degrees.

On the floor were three large, tightly closed boxes that had been brought over from Hospital Number One early that morning. When Reed looked in the window, he saw that Dr. Cook had seated himself on one of the beds and was staring at the boxes. Without raising his eyes, he drawled, "Those are the ones, eh?"

Reed said, "That's right."

Cook continued to stare at the boxes, as did Folk and Jernegan. There was a hard, flat look in their eyes. Folk was already perspiring freely. Finally, Cook shrugged and stood up.

"All right. Let's get at it. The sooner we start, the sooner we'll be done."

Each man knelt beside a box and undid the twine that circled it. Cook put his hands on the lid of the box he had selected, ready to pull it upward. He glanced up at Reed. The eyes of Folk and Jernegan came up with his gaze.

"All right, Major?"

"Go ahead."

"Go ahead."

The three men breathed deeply, readying themselves. Simultaneously, they raised the lids, bringing them up quickly. Reed's hands knotted themselves into fists. There in the boxes were the blankets, the sheets, the hospital gowns, the pillows, the underwear, and towels of men who had died of the fever. The articles were stained with blood, stiff and crusted over with the black vomit and excrement of the sickness. A foul odor, the yellow-green stench of death, filled the hot little room. Reed took a wrenching step backward from the window. He saw Folk throw his hands up to his mouth, heard him make a long gagging sound. The corpsman whirled away from the boxes and, bent low, ran out through the front door. He was followed swiftly by Cook and Jernegan.

Cook was the first to come back into the room. He ducked his head in through the door and grinned sheepishly across at Reed. His long face was coated with a grayish film of icy sweat. He wiped the back of his hand across his mouth.

"Sorry, Major."

"Don't apologise," Reed said, forcing a grin, working hard to keep his own throat muscles from contracting. "You came back. That's all that matters."

Cook stuck one fisted hand against his hip. His eyes ran round the walls, but they carefully avoided the boxes.

"Twenty nights we've got to spend in here, Major?"

"Exactly twenty."

Cook leaned back and glanced at Jernegan and Folk, who were out of Reed's sight.

"All right, boys," he said. "We've had our chance to get over our weak stomachs. Let's get moved in."

Jernegan and Folk, dead white and grinning weakly, appeared in the doorway. They followed Cook across the bare floor to the boxes. Taking all their courage in hand, they reached down into the boxes and began to pull out the filthy articles.

"Shake everything out thoroughly," Reed instructed. "Spread them around. Do everything in your power to contaminate the whole place."

Dutifully, the volunteers followed instructions. They tried to make a joke out of the entire process, in a valiant effort to contain their revulsion. They placed the sheets and blankets with military neatness on the cots. They removed pillows and stuffed them into cases streaked and splashed with black. They draped towels and underwear over the beds. When they were done, they shoved the boxes into a corner of the room.

Then began a task that was far more difficult than anything they had done thus far. At Cook's signal, they stripped off their uniforms and put on the hospital gowns in which men had died. Reed saw that Jernegan was trembling uncontrollably. The stench in the room seemed so thick as to be visible. Folk slipped a gown over his head. He smoothed it out and gazed down its stained front. His teeth began to chatter, as if he were out somewhere in the cold. Cook did all in his power to seem unconcerned about his surroundings. He sat down on the edge of his cot and, with a wide grin, surveyed Folk and Jernegan.

"You look very nice," he drawled. "Now off to bed."

Jernegan and Folk exchanged glances, as if they were swimmers, each waiting for the other to be the first to plunge into an icy stream. Suddenly Jernegan cursed, threw back the soiled blankets, and sprawled flat on his back on the cot. More slowly, Folk crawled into his bed. He carefully placed his arms on the outside of the blankets, keeping the rim of the bedding away from his throat.

Reed felt a little of the tension go out of him. He glanced over at Agramonte and Carroll, and saw the admiration in their faces for the three men in the room. He looked back at the volunteers.

"Thank you, gentlemen," he said. "There's no need for me to tell you how grateful I am for what you are doing. We'll see you in the morning. I know it's going to be hard, but try to stick it out. Don't leave unless you can't stand it a minute longer."

"We'll stick it out, Major," Cook said. He was stretched out on his bed and upthrust on one elbow. "Right, Jernegan? Folk?"

Jernegan said, "Right."

Folk nodded. He was staring straight up at the ceiling, his teeth clamped tightly together.

The doctors walked away from the shack, leaving the three volunteers to accustom themselves, if that could be, to their surroundings. The doctors walked in silence, their heads down, their expressions thoughtful. At last, kicking at a stone that the Spaniards had overlooked, Carroll said,

"Well, it's filthy in there, but at least they're safe from the fever. We all know that the fomites are harmless."

"We *think* they're safe," Reed corrected him. "And we *think* the fomites are harmless. We should know for certain within a very few days."

Six days after Cook, Folk, and Jernegan had entered the Infected Clothing Building for the first time, a desperate Reed returned to the first part of his plan. He had no complaints concerning the second part; it was proceeding according to his expectations. The three volunteers, passing their nights among the filthy trappings of death and their days huddled together in an isolation tent nearby, were showing no signs of the fever. But neither were Kissinger, Moran, and the Spaniard. They had to fall ill, he told himself. The success of the entire project depended on it.

On December 5, he summoned Kissinger to the recently completed Mosquito House and subjected him to another series of bites. It was the third time, and he took the bites of five insects, two of which had fed on fatal cases 15 days and 19 days before. He gazed ruefully at the ugly welts rising on his arms, and said, "I don't think I'm ever going to get it, sir. I'll wager I'm a natural immune."

Carroll, standing just behind him, grinned, "Don't be too sure about that. Third time's the charm, you know."

"That," snorted Reed, who was in no mood for levity, "is an old wives' tale."

Carroll shrugged, still grinning. "Suppose we wait and see."

They waited—and they saw. By the late afternoon of December 8, Kissinger was complaining of a headache. The next day, he was carried over to the fever ward at Columbia; he was now nauseated and feverish, and the ache that had started behind his eyes had spread downward into his back and arms. The tell-tale color came into his face during the following morning. The diagnosis was simple to make. The young man had a perfect case of yellow fever!

Now, with dizzying swiftness, the tide of battle turned in Reed's favor. Three Spaniards, subjected to bites at the time Kissinger was falling ill, came down with the fever by December 15, with the result that their fellow countrymen, realizing at last the true danger of the work at hand and forgetting completely their cherished $100, fled the camp in panic. Reed was annoyed with their untimely departure, but only momentarily, for his mind was too full of triumph to harbor anger long.

He could think of nothing but the fact that he had four laboratory produced cases of fever on his hands—cases that, thank God, were proving to be light ones, with full recovery for their victims assured. Four cases!

For the first time in its 19-year history, the mosquito theory had given definitive evidence of its validity. The doubt that had shadowed the illnesses of Lazear, Carroll, and even Private Dean no longer mattered. Kissinger and the Spaniards had contracted the disease under the strictest of controls. There was simply nothing else in the world that could have given the men the infection.

In his jubilation, Reed wrote his wife to say that God had granted him the privilege to participate in a work that, exclusive of the discoveries of the diptheria antitoxin and Koch's tuberculosis bacillus, would rank as the most important scientific accomplishment of the 19th century.

But, happy as he was, he was not blind to certain hard truths. He knew that the four cases constituted no more than a splendid start towards truth. More proof would be required before the hard-headed scientists of the world accepted Finlay's theory as solid, incontestable fact. And they had every right to demand further proof. He had but one experiment to his credit, and it was their tough, careful tradition not to formulate or accept a possible truth on the basis of a single test.

He smiled grimly to himself. He was ready for their tough, careful tradition. In a few days, as soon as Cook, Folk, and Jernegan were released from the Infected Clothing Building, he would launch the second part of his over-all plan. It would give the scientists all the proof they required.

Over in the Infected Clothing Building, there was much relief at the news that Kissinger and the three Spaniards were down with the yellow jack. Cook, Folk, and Jernegan, when they had first entered the little shack, had not had any guarantee that they could emerge untouched by the fever. For, after all, the belief that the fomites were harmless was nothing more than an unproved idea. But now they were fairly well convinced that they were safe. They could never enjoy their surroundings, but at least they could endure them with easier minds for the remainder of their stay.

That stay ended on December 19. The three volunteers came out of the shack for the last time and, before rushing off to a long-anticipated bath, stood in a tight little group near the door, gulping in great draughts of clean air and pounding each other on the back. They said that, because they had left the building daily, they had never been given the chance to accustom themselves to the stench; it had struck them anew each night. Laughing now, they recollected the anger they had felt when Reed had ordered additional bedding and clothing brought in from Las Animas and Hospital Number One; they remembered how the vile stuff, heaped on the beds and on the floor, had given the room the appearance of a nightmarish laundry. But now they were done with the building and the experiment. And they were perfectly well. They evidenced not one sign of the fever.

With a deep sense of admiration Reed congratulated them on their revolting but harmless ordeal. He sent them off to their bath, and then, as a double check on the experiment, he immediately installed two new volunteers in the shack, James Hanberry and Edward Weatherwalks. Without harm, they slept among the trappings of death for 20 nights, suffering the identical discomforts that had plagued their predecessors. They, in turn, were followed by James Hildebrand and Thomas England, with the exact same results. Towards the end of January, Reed called the experiment off. The harmlessness of the fomites was firmly established.

By December 21, Reed was ready to launch the second part of the attack on the fomites theory. Part one of his plan had given every indication that a mosquito was responsible for the spread of the fever. Part two had illustrated that there was no danger to be found in the filthiest of houses infested with fomites.

Now, to further smash the fomites theory and especially to remove any lingering doubts as to the truth of the mosquito theory, Reed planned to demonstrate that a house as clean as a surgical ampitheater and without fomites in it became a place of death when visited by an infected *Culex fasciatus*.

For the experiment, he selected John J. Moran, who had suffered no ill effects from the bites taken on the 26th and 29th of November. He walked the volunteer up to the one-room Mosquito House, passing Cook, Folk, and Jernegan on the way. The three veterans of the fomites test gaped at the sight of Moran, and they had every right to do so. Moran was freshly bathed, shaved, and combed. His skin glowed from the strong soap he had used. He was dressed in a spotless hospital gown and a robe of snowy white. Cook remarked drily that "some people have all the luck."

The two men entered the Mosquito House and found Carroll, Agramonte, and two Medical Corps privates awaiting them. Reed explained to Moran that Carroll and Agramonte would serve as observers to the experiment, to attest to the strict control under which it was being conducted. The two privates, he added, were to play a part later on in the work. Moran nodded. His eyes went round the interior of the small building.

Originally constructed to shelter the fragile *Culex fasciatus* after the storm of mid-November as well as to serve for the present experiment, the Mosquito House had been painstakingly readied for this morning's work. The room was divided in half by a partition constructed, from floor to ceiling of fine mesh screen. The half of the room in which Moran now stood contained two steel cots, as yet not covered with blankets. On the other side of the partition was another cot, but this one was covered with a crisp white sheet, freshly laundered and pressed; the mattress had been recently cleaned with steam. There were large windows, all of them heavily screened, in the north and south walls, allowing through ventilation. The room had the odor of hospital antiseptic to it. It had just been thoroughly scrubbed down with disinfectant. Reed and Moran stepped to the partition. Buzzing sounds came faintly from the opposite side of the screen.

Moran hunched his shoulders slightly. "How many, Major?"

Reed knew what the man had in mind. "Fifteen," he said. "The number we originally planned. Carroll and Agramonte turned them loose about five minutes ago."

Moran touched the screen. "There's no chance that any of them will escape?"

"Not a one," Reed assured him. "The tiniest mosquito couldn't squirm his way through this mesh, or through that on the windows. The insects will be in there until they die or until we go in and kill them."

The volunteer made a wry face. "Well, you've certainly fixed it up so that I'll have to take all the bites I can stand, haven't you?"

"Indeed we have. Everyone of the mosquitoes in there has been fed on a serious case." Reed put his hand on Moran's shoulder. "Now, it's up to you to give them a good meal. I think 20 to 30 minutes should do it for this time."

"All right, sir."

Reed murmured, "Good luck," and Moran, flashing him a smile, quickly opened a small door in the partition and stepped through it, closing it just as quickly behind him. He removed his robe and tossed it across the foot of the bed. Then he lay down on the white sheet, putting himself flat on his back and placing his bare arms straight down at his sides. He took a deep breath and seemed to relax. Reed took his watch out from beneath his tunic. The hour was 12 o'clock noon.

Carroll, Agramonte, and the two Medical Corpsmen closed in round Reed, their eyes on Moran and their ears tuned to the buzzing sounds. The room was dead silent, except for the buzzing and the heavy breathing of the men, for two minutes. Moran had his eyes closed. He looked as if he had fallen asleep. Then he spoke. His voice was soft, but it held a sharp note of excitement.

"I've got a customer."

Moran raised his head slightly and, as if fascinated by a sight he had never seen before, watched a mosquito settle on his right wrist. The insect went into its biting position and drove its silver beak beneath the skin. Moran watched it fly away. A moment later, he winced and instinctively went to slap the side of his neck. He caught himself in time. He lay motionless, staring up at the ceiling, his lips thinning now and again, as the mosquitoes sought him out.

Finally, at the end of 20 minutes, Reed called, "Time."

Moran, letting a sigh escape him, pulled himself off the bed and came over to the partition. Reed stared at his face, his

[*180*]

neck, and his arms. They were speckled here and there with ugly yellow welts. Reed nodded his satisfaction.

"That's it for now, Jim," he said. "We'll try again early this evening and first thing tomorrow morning."

"Good enough," Moran said. He waited until the buzzing seemed to have collected at a distant point and then he slipped through the little door.

He had been bitten seven times.

Moran underwent the ordeal again at the times specified by Reed. Then he returned to his tent, under instructions to take his temperature every three hours. He lay down on his cot and began to read a novel that he had started some days ago. He had a good, confident feeling about the whole experiment. He had failed to contract the fever after the bitings of the 26th and 29th of November, but the current work was far different from those first jobs. Most important of all, this time he was covered with welts. The poison of yellow jack *had* to be in him. He was going to get it this time, all right—just as sure as shooting, he was going to get it.

Unless—terrible thought—he was a natural immune.

He shrugged that disquieting idea out of mind. He focused his eyes on the book. He begain his time of waiting.

On the night of December 21, the two Medical Corpsmen who had stood watching with Reed that morning began to play their part in the experiment. They carried their blankets over to the Mosquito House and spread them out on the two bunks in that half of the room not infested with mosquitoes. From time to time they heard, from beyond the partition, a faint buzzing sound. They sat down on the bunks and gazed at each other.

Then they shook their heads and agreed that this man Reed was the most ingenious human being they had ever met.

The job that he had designed for them was simple, but, if the experiment worked, so effective that it would destroy all doubt of Dr. Finlay's theory. They were to sleep in the side of the room separated from the mosquitoes by only that fine mesh screen for 18 nights.

If they remained in perfect health while Moran fell ill—What further proof could the medical world then ask for?

Christmas Day dawned gray and cold. A steady, chilling wind found its way from the sea to Camp Lazear. Reed went over to Columbia to visit friends, and Moran spent the morning dutifully recording his temperature. By noontime, he knew that something was happening. An ache that had been a vague blur far back in his head at sunrise had sharpened and had localized itself directly behind his eyes. His temperature at 1 o'clock was up to 100 degrees. He felt excitement surge through him. He began reaching for the thermometer every few minutes.

He was up half a degree by 2 o'clock. He had suffered several chills. Perhaps it was his imagination, but he thought he felt the beginnings of pain in his arms and legs. No, too soon for that, he told himself. But there was no mistaking the pain in his head. It was throbbing now behind his eyes, and it was the sort of headache that was making him feel nauseated. He moved to a little mirror tacked to the centerpole of the tent. He stared at himself. He grinned with hard satisfaction. His face was flushed and slick with sweat; his eyes were bloodshot. Perfect! Perfect!

Then, suddenly, he was angry with Reed for being away. He swung about, the pain behind his eyes exploding with the movement, and walked on unsteady legs to the tent flap. He peered out at the grounds and felt a chill tremble through him at the touch of the wind from the sea. Where the devil was Reed? The man was due back at 3 o'clock. He should never have left in the first place.

Moran took hold of his anger. He knew that it was compounded of his illness and his impatience to share his wonderful knowledge with the doctor. He went back to his cot and threw himself down on it. The canvas walls of the tent whirled above him. He clamped his eyes shut, pressing the heels of his hands against his closed lids. Where was Reed? Calm down, boy, he told himself. There were still 45 minutes left until 3 o'clock.

He could not stay where he was for more than a few minutes. He pulled himself up, swinging his legs off the cot and planting his feet firmly on the plank floor. He took his temperature again. It took him a long while to focus his gaze on the tiny lines of the thermometer. What he saw made the effort worthwhile. One hundred and one degrees. Good boy! You're doing just fine.

He held his face in his hands and closed his eyes again. He saw little bursts of yellow and red; they seemed to come dancing from far away; they popped when they got up close and then appeared again at their starting point. He tried to concentrate on them. They took his mind off the nausea.

He caught himself as he started to fall to one side, and he realized that he had dropped off to sleep for a few moments. He fumbled for his watch on the little table alongside the cot. Three o'clock straight up. He got to his feet, angry again. The Major should be here! Right now! He lurched through the front opening of the tent.

[*183*]

Then all the anger went out of him. He sighted Reed driving a buggy onto the grounds. The Major came directly to him. Moran stood very still, the wind putting icy fingers inside him, and he knew that he was smiling a silly smile, and he knew that there was nothing he could do about it. Reed halted the buggy near him and dropped to the ground.

"Merry Christmas, Jim—"

The words died on Reed's lips. His eyes went narrow. He came swiftly to Moran. He stared hard into his face. He saw the silly grin. He saw the flushed complexion, the film of perspiration, the bloodshot eyes.

Moran said, "I think I've got it, sir."

Reed said, "I know you do."

Then, suddenly, they were gripping each other by the shoulders and they were standing there, swaying in the wind, and they were laughing. It was the eager, deep-throated laughter of victory.

Ten minutes later Reed was sitting by himself in Moran's tent. The volunteer was already in an ambulance on his way to the isolation ward at Camp Columbia. Reed was due to follow him, but he wanted a moment or so to rest, to collect his thoughts.

Outside, the news of Moran's illness was spreading through the camp, from the American volunteers to the soldiers on guard duty to the new contingent of Spanish workers that Agramonte had recently fetched from Tiscornia Immigration Station. There were shouts and yells riding on the cold air, but Reed paid them no attention. His mind was completely taken up with the magnificent knowledge that he had

[184]

come to the end of a long trail. There was still work to be done
with the fever, yes, but the high point of his investigations had
been reached ten minutes ago, when he had stared into
Moran's feverish eyes.

Those eyes had told him that, in the cleanest of surroundings, Moran had come upon the yellow death. Now, provided
that the two Medical Corpsmen over in the Mosquito House
did not fall ill—and it was impossible that they should—the villain of the yellow death had been identified beyond controversy.
The Yellow Fever Commission had established beyond doubt
the method by which the fever was spread. With the knowledge in hand, a campaign could now be launched to wipe out
the *Culex fasciatus*, a campaign that would see the evil flame of
life go out of the yellow jack.

He heard himself murmur a prayer for Moran's safety. At
the same time, he was calmly certain that the volunteer would
recover. Thus far, he had known the miracle of miracles, not a
single death in all the experiments at Camp Lazear. In the experiments remaining, experiments that would round out the
picture of the fever, he would have to ask other men to pit their
lives against death. Yet, somehow, at this moment, he was posi-
tive that he would travel the rest of the way with that same
miraculous record. He was right.

He came slowly to his feet. For the first time in days, he was
truly excited. Unlike his first week at Camp Lazear, when he had
fretted over Kissinger's failure to fall ill, he had experienced no
great concern over whether or not Moran would contract the
fever. He had simply known that he would. In the light of the
fate that had befallen Kissinger and the three Spaniards, there
was nothing else that could have happened to Moran. But now,

with the realization of victory full upon, excitement was a living thing in him. He wanted to have Agramonte and Carroll here, so that they could share his joy. They were spending Christmas at Havana. He must telephone them as soon as he arrived at Camp Columbia. And he must telephone Finlay. They all must know of the success of the work in which they had participated. Finlay, he knew, would be delirious with happiness; 19 years of scorn could fall from his little shoulders. What a Christmas gift that would be!

Suddenly, a wave of sadness passed through Reed. If there were only one other person here, then his own joy would be complete. Jesse Lazear. To him more than anyone else on the Yellow Fever Commission, this Christmas day belonged. For it was he who had first looked with faith on Finlay's maligned theory. It was he who had worked so hard to convince his fellow doctor's of the theory's validity. It was he—Reed's eyes misted over. If only Jesse could be here. Then he shook his head, clearing his vision. Deep within him was the quiet conviction that Jesse Lazear was well aware of the splendor of this day, of this very moment.

Slowly, Walter Reed left the tent and emerged into a world that, in a very few days, would be a finer place in which to live.

Chapter 13

A Final Note

Walter Reed and the Yellow Fever Commission concluded their work in Cuba by early February, 1901. January was devoted mainly to the third part of Reed's plan: the demonstration that the germ responsible for the fever was, as scientists had long suspected, resident in the blood stream. The experiment involved five men, four of them Americans. Two cubic centimeters of blood, withdrawn from a fever victim, were injected into Warren G. Jernegan. He fell ill within four days, at which time a sample of his blood was passed into William Olson, who was placed in isolation on the 11th. The experiment was concluded with Wallace Forbes and John Andrus. Both contracted the fever within four days after their injections. A Spanish immigrant who participated in the series remained perfectly fit. Because he had also failed to respond to a bite of a *Culex fasciatus*, it was felt that he was a natural immune or, unknown to himself, had had the fever.

The experiment was judged a success. In addition to pinpointing scientifically the location of the germ, it also demonstrated that the germ was in the blood stream for several days early in the disease and that its passage through the *Culex fasciatus*, though necessary to its spread, was not vital to its development.

The puzzle of why the fever could suddenly appear again in a house several weeks after the initial victims had recovered or had died was solved. In a series of tests, Reed proved that a house is in danger for as long as an infected *Culex fasciatus* remains hidden within it, for the yellow jack exists with the mosquito for the rest of its life. Levi Folk, Clyde West, James Hanberry, and Charles Sonntag took bites from mosquitoes that had fed on fever victims from 39 to more than 60 days earlier. All the men fell ill. All of them recovered.

John Andrus took part in the Commission's concluding work. Dr. Carlos Finlay had always advanced the idea that the offspring of an infected *Culex fasciatus* were capable of spreading the disease. Andrus disproved this part of Finlay's theory by submitting to the stings of the offspring of several infected mosquitoes. He remained perfectly fit.

On February 6, speaking before the Pan-American Medical Congress at Havana, Reed made public the results of the work of his Commission, earning for Finlay the praise that the old man had deserved for 19 years. Reed announced that the fever, that deadly enemy of the world's warmer climates for centuries now, could be controlled in the simplest ways. The fighters of disease simply had to wipe out the *Culex fasciatus*, destroy its breeding places, and keep it from reaching any new fever victims.

William Crawford Gorgas was appointed to follow Reed's suggestions. In the streets of Havana, his men attacked gutters, rain barrels, cesspools, collections of stagnant water; in the houses of the city, they wiped out the fragile little insect wherever they found it, cleaning dry and spotless the haunts that it so dearly loved. Within 90 days, Gorgas' efforts bore fruit. For the first time since 1649, Havana was free of the yellow death. Gorgas won for himself international fame when he applied the very same techniques in Panama, destroying the fever and malaria there, and making possible the construction of the Panama Canal. With commendable modesty, he always said that he was simply following in the footsteps of Dr. Walter Reed.

Those techniques were used with great success throughout Cuba in the next years, and in the southern and western United States, British Honduras, and several large cities in Brazil. They marked the beginning of the downfall of yellow fever throughout all the warmer climates of the world.

Reed returned to the United States before the spring of 1901. He left Agramonte and Carroll in Cuba to pursue other issues involving the fever. Agramonte, at the end of his service with the Army, remained in his island country, becoming professor of bacteriology and experimental pathology at the University of Havana.

Carroll, before the summer of 1901 was done, found why the Commission in those first investigations of the germ of yellow fever had, like all other searchers before them, failed to locate it. Taking a quantity of infected blood, he

[*189*]

strained it through a porcelain filter capable of trapping the smallest known bacteria. He injected the resultant serum into three American volunteers. When they fell ill with yellow jack, he knew what he had always suspected: that the cause of the fever is an ultra-microscopic, filterable virus.

As years passed, other facts came to light. A commission of the Rockefeller Foundation, operating in West Africa in 1927, discovered that the rhesus monkey is capable of taking the fever from a mosquito bite. Later, mice and hedge-hogs were shown not to be immune.

Following years showed the medical world that Reed and his associates had conquered only one type of yellow fever, now commonly referred to as "urban yellow fever." Another type of yellow fever, called "jungle yellow fever," was sighted in Brazilian areas free of the *Culex fasciatus*. Reed had always known that the disease followed a man-mosquito-man pattern, but he had never fathomed exactly how the sickness got into the initial victim in a district. The original source of the fever had been beyond his knowledge.

Current belief holds that "jungle yellow fever" is the permanent endemic source of the disease and that from it epidemics spread out to the cities. It is now known that those epidemics are carried on the wings of 17 different types of mosquito, excluding the *Culex fasciatus* (now catalogued as *Aedes aegypti*).

Dr. Max Theiler of the Rockefeller Foundation discovered, in 1937, an excellent vaccine to protect against the fever. It has been injected into more than 100,000,000 persons in the years since its development.

Great attention and honor were bestowed on Reed upon his return to the United States. Messages of congratulation came to him from over the world. He was asked to speak before medical and health societies. Harvard, in the summer of 1902, awarded him an M.A. degree. A few weeks later, he received from the University of Michigan an L.L.D. degree. He was appointed Librarian of the Surgeon General's Library, in Washington, D.C.

Throughout those triumphant months of 1901 and 1902, Reed, quite correctly, refused to accept the full share of credit for the magnificent Cuban accomplishment. The credit, he said, belonged to every member of the Yellow Fever Commission and to the many brave men who worked for them. They had all worked together, sharing the disappointment and the heartbreak and the danger and the exhaustion. Now, they must all share in the glory.

Reed soon found himself back in the full swing of class and laboratory work at the Army Medical School. In November of 1902, he fell slightly ill; it was nothing, he told himself, just a persistent indigestion and a feeling of tiredness, obviously the result of too many months of work and excitement. It would soon pass. He was just 50 years old. There were so many things about yellow fever that he still had to learn, so many investigations that he dreamed of making.

By mid-month, his discomfort was such that he visited his personal physician, Major W. C. Borden. Borden's examination revealed that the "indigestion" was really an infected appendix. Borden ordered immediate surgery. That surgery was performed on November 17. It came too late. By that time, the appendix had burst and its poison had spread throughout

Reed's slender body. He held onto life for a week; then, at the very height of his career, Walter Reed died quietly in the pre-dawn hours of November 23, 1902.

The honors bestowed on him in death far exceeded those given him in life. A bronze bust of him was placed in the main entrance of the Army Medical Museum. A United States postage stamp was printed in his honor. A gold medal commemorating his great work was ordered struck by Congress. And, greatest tribute of all, the giant Army medical center at Washington D.C. today bears his name.

But he was a simple man, a gentle man, and possibly the tribute that gave him the greatest pleasure is the one that is inscribed above his grave in Arlington National Cemetery. Written there are the words that President Eliot of Harvard spoke when he awarded the gray haired physician the degree of Master of Arts. *He gave to man control over that dreadful scourge, yellow fever.*